New & Improved
3rd Edition
The Bead Directory

400 of the best sources for beads and bead supplies!

The most comprehensive
collection of bead sources
available.

Linda Benmour

ACKNOWLEDGMENTS

This book is dedicated to MSB
Once again there are many people to thank for helping put this Directory together including all the beadaholics who sent information and gave me their ideas to make the third edition even better. Thank you Milt, Alice (and her infamous red pen), Kim, Jody, Leah, Jane, Linda L., Jill (the Dbase Queen), my mother for listening to all my ideas and always saying "you'll do great"; Uncle Natch for those brief but inspiring letters; my family; Jean Astrinsky who once again opened the Orb Weaver for use in judging the Cover Bead Competition; Chris Carmer and Rosalie Day of North Vernon Abstract for their copy machine; all the bead stores who sold so many Directories; the beadmakers who contributed and Maggie!

In memory of my father, the world's greatest salesman, and Aunt Phyllis -- your smiles live on. We miss you!

First Printing 1995
Copyright © 1995, by Linda Benmour
ISBN 1-883153-18-2   Printed in the United States
Published by Ben-Stone Press and The Bead Directory, P.O. Box 10103, Oakland, CA 94610. All rights reserved.

Additional copies available for $18.95 plus $3.75 s&h payable to The Bead Directory, P.O. Box 10103-D, Oakland, CA 94610 USA.

Art Director: Milton Firestone, my Genius
Art Assistant: Kim Osibin, the Idea Queen
Cover & Ad Design: Robin Simmons, Simmons Design, Pasadena CA
Proofreading: Milton Firestone
Editing: Alice Scherer, Director, Center for the Study of Beadwork
Photography: George Post Photography, Richmond, CA
Distribution and Mail House: Jill Jarkovsky, the Genius

TABLE OF CONTENTS

Table of Contents

Table of Contents

INTRODUCTION

Thank you for buying the Third Edition of *The Bead Directory*.
We know you will enjoy this new and improved 3rd Edition. We read
every Reply Card and incorporated your ideas to improve this edition.
There are now separate sections for beadmakers, mail order only
businesses, and beadmaking supplies. You'll also find more discount
coupons and many new books and videos. The response to each
edition keeps growing and we appreciate your continued support. It
is a lot of hard work to put this Directory together and most of it is
done by one person. We're not a big company with a lot of staff, we're
a small business working hard to bring you the very best Directory
possible. Use the coupons and buy from the bead stores that make
The Bead Directory possible. Please return the Reply Card, we want to
hear from all of our readers.

MAILING LABELS ARE AVAILABLE FOR ALL OF THE BUSINESSES IN THE DIRECTORY

A lot of people use *The Bead Directory* to create a mailing list of their
own. All of the business names listed in the Directory are available on
disc or labels. Save yourself time and money and send a business size
SASE for an order form.

THE BEADMAKERS

The beads on the front and back cover are the first and second place winners of our annual Cover Bead Competition. Photos of the third and fourth place winners and a group photo of some of the great beads entered are in the color insert. The judges were Robert K. Liu, Editor of Ornament; Kim Osibin, Beadmaker and Designer; Suzanne Stern, Beadmaker and Designer; and the assistants were Milton Firestone, Art Director; Jody McDonnell, Owner of Legendary Beads and Jean Astrinsky, Owner of the Orb Weaver.

Listed below are the names and addresses of the beadmakers. When writing, please tell them you saw their beads in *The Bead Directory*.

Front Cover: Michael Max, a glass artist and educator, has been exploring hot glass processes and teaching for over 14 years. His inspiration for design and form comes from shapes and processes in nature and from his own experience of discovering how glass wants to move. Exhibited nationally, Michael teaches workshops at his studio in Seattle. Modern Alchemy, 3026 NW 60th Street, Seattle WA 98107

Back Cover: Kristina Logan, 42 Court Street, No. 3, Exeter, NH 03833. **Third place**:, Cynthia Toops, CD Beads, polymer clay artist, 2514 E. Spring Street, Seattle, WA 98122. **Fourth place**: Donna Milliron, Arrow Springs, 4570 Tennessee Drive, Shingle Springs, CA 95682 and Lucy Bergamini, Vitriesse Glass, P. O. Box 23, Weston, VT 05143.

A list of the beadmakers featured in the group photo in the color insert are:

Tom Andre, Andre Glass; Virginia Flowers; Heather Trimlett; Jim Jones, BullFrog Beads; Stevi Belle, Winged Woman Creations; Mary Mullaney, Heron Glass; Dan Adams, CD Beads; Carolyn Noga; Leah Fairbanks, Gardens of Glass; Bernadette Fuentes; Mary Kennedy, Glass Gallery; Tom Holland; Bruce St. John Maher; Molly Vaughan Haskins, Laughing Glass; Loren Stump, Adventure In Glass; and Harmon Schmelzenbach, Nyala Enterprises.

To order a copy of the group photo of the glass beadmakers, send a SASE for an order form. Prints are available in several sizes.

HOW TO USE THE BEAD DIRECTORY

YOUR COMMENTS ARE IMPORTANT TO US
Please complete the Reply Card in the back of the book and we'll send you a **free bead catalog.**

Use The Bead Directory for mail order sources, take it with you when you travel and use the Discount Coupons to save money. **When contacting any of the businesses listed, make sure you tell them you saw their listing in** *The Bead Directory.* *The Bead Directory* will save you many hours of looking for sources so you can spend your time creating beautiful beadwork and buying more beads.

Businesses are listed geographically and cross-referenced. Each listing contains information that was provided by the business. If something is missing it is because the business did not provide that information or that information does not pertain to that particular business. The following explanations will make it easier to understand the listings. If you find a listing that is out of date, please write and tell us so we can keep the Directory as current as possible. If any of the coupons or bead bazaar listings are out of date, please send a business size SASE and we'll send you current dates and coupons.

Payment - Local Cks - the business takes local checks only.
Checks/Cks - the business accepts local and out-of-state checks.
MC - Master Card. AE - American Express. Disc - Discover Card
M.O. - Money Order. COD - Cash on delivery. Some businesses may take other charge cards, always ask as policies may change.
SASE - Self-addressed stamped envelope.

Minimum order. When the business has stated an amount, it is listed. Many businesses have minimum amounts for retail, wholesale, mail order and charge card orders, always ask.

Exhibiting at - Many businesses exhibit at bead bazaars, gem and jewelry shows, craft fairs, conferences, etc., throughout the United States. Call the business to ask for dates and locations.

Remember to call ahead before visiting a store.
Always call to verify hours, forms of payment, minimum orders and other information listed. Businesses move a lot, phone numbers change and store hours change. The information listed here was current at the time of printing.

THE BEAD GALLERY
201 Seward Street
Juneau, AK 99801
Phone: 907-586-3223
Hours: Mon-Sat 11 - 5
Owner: Chris Prussing
Specialty: Neat stuff at a fair price!

Payment: Checks-MC-Visa
Retail: Yes
Mail Order: $15 minimum
Catalog: SASE for a
   product list
Custom Work: Yes
Finished Pieces: Yes

Funky location, eccentric sales help. If staff moves too quickly, things fall on them. Right out of Northern Exposure.

BEAD HEAVEN
3901 Old Seward Hwy #3E
Anchorage AK 99503
Phone: 907-563-5183
Hours: Mon-Fri 10-9 Sat 10-7
   Sun 12 - 6
Owner: Jan Schorg-Forsyth
Specialty: Semi-precious stone and glass beads

Payment: Local Cks-MC-Visa
Retail: Yes
Mail Order: Yes
Catalog: Available soon
Classes: Call for schedule

The largest bead store in Alaska, specializing in beads and findings from all over the world. Well organized with walls full of bins with beads of all types. Also one-of-a-kind, antique, sterling silver, lots of seed beads, how-to books and classes for adults and children. The staff is always available to help with projects.

BEADS AND THINGS
537 2nd Avenue
Fairbanks, AK 99701
Phone: 907-456-2323
   800-478-2323
Hours: Mon-Sat 10-6 Sun 12-5
Owner: Ann M. Goessel
Specialty: Authentic Alaskan Native arts and crafts.
Exhibiting at: Alaska Federation of Natives Convention, Anchorage, 3rd week of October.

Payment: Cks-MC-Visa-AE-Disc
Retail: Yes
Wholesale: Yes
Mail Order: Yes
Catalog: Yes
Classes: Call for information
Custom Work: Call for quote

Carvings from St. Lawrence Island, and North Slope Villages. Athabascan beadwork including slippers, boots, barrettes, pins and earrings, bead kits and sewing supplies. Most beaded items are one-of-a-kind. Over 1,000 different beads, felt design patterns, and books.

KILLER BEADS

P. O. Box 110287
Anchorage, AK 99511
Phone: 907-272-1807
Hours: By appointment only
Owners: Tamara Johannes, Terri Atwell
Specialty: Handcrafted jewelry

Payment: Cks
Retail: Yes
Wholesale : $150 minimum
Mail Order: Special arrangement
Restringing: Call for quote
Custom Work: Call for quote

Women-owned business specializing in handcrafted jewelry using antique and unique contemporary beads and metals. These unusual beads are sold to collectors through occasional private collector sales.

SPIRIT BEADS

174 S. Franklin
  #108 Emporium Mall
Juneau, AK 99801
Phone: 907-463-3220
Hours: Tues-Fri 12-5 Sat 12-4
Owner: Salty Hanes

Payment: Cks-MC-Visa
Retail: Yes
Wholesale: Yes
Mail Order: Yes
Restringing: Call for quote
Finished pieces: Yes

All sizes of glass seed beads, semiprecious, Austrian crystal, trade, beads, chevrons, charms, findings, buttons, felt, leather, looms and books. Beading classes for all ages

ARIZONA

THE BEAD CONNECTION

6538 B East Tanque Verde Road
Tucson, AZ 85715
Phone: 602-885-3020
FAX: 602-885-7950
Hours: Mon-Sat 10-5
Owner: Nancy A. Ferguson
Specialty: Glass beads
Exhibiting at: Arizona Bead Society bazaars.

Payment: Cks-MC-Visa
Retail: Yes
Wholesale: $20 minimum
Mail Order: $10 minimum
Classes: Call for schedule
Restringing: Call for prices
Custom Work: Call
Finished Pieces: Yes

Friendly shopping environment. Large variety of beads and charms displayed for easy access. Ongoing classes, custom orders welcome and always something new and unusual.

BEAD IT!

152 South Montezuma
Prescott, AZ 86303
Phone: 602-445-9234
FAX: 602-445-6270
Hours: Daily 10-5
Owner: Alessandra Scamardo
Specialty: Czech and ethnic

Payment: Cks-MC-Visa-Disc
Retail: Yes
Mail Order: $25 minimum
Catalog: Call for cost
Classes: Seasonal schedule
Finished Pieces: Yes

Located in historic downtown Prescott, just a few doors away from
The Bead Museum at the back of an art gallery. Large selection of
Czech and Japanese seed beads, unusual beads and components from
around the world, a wide assortment of findings, tools, supplies and
books. Knowledgeable staff will assist you with design and techniques. Also lampworked beads by contemporary artists. Vintage
German, milagros, Bali silver and lots of ethnic beads.

THE BEAD SOURCE

7051 North Oracle Road
Tucson, AZ 85704
Phone: 602-575-0130
Hours: Mon-Sat 10-5:30 Sun 10-4
Owner: Pam Preslar
Specialty: Seed beads
  and Austrian crystals

Payment: Cks-MC-Visa
Retail: Yes
Wholesale: Yes
Mail Order: $50 minimum
Catalog: Free
Classes: Call for schedule
Finished Pieces: Yes

Exhibiting at: Tucson Gem Show September and February at the
Rodeway Inn, at Grant & I-10.

Sunlight dances through the seed beads and Swarovski crystal beads
in the window and glistens off tray after tray of exotic beads throughout this cheerfully appointed shop. An enormous variety of classes
and a wide variety of seed beads, turquoise, coral, exotic glass, metal
and charms. Large assortment of books, supplies and tools.

BEADS & ADORNABLES

7163 N. 58th Drive
Glendale, AZ 85301
Phone: 602-930-7395
FAX: 602-930-1157
Hours: Mon-Sat 10-5 Thurs 10-8
Owner: Cheryl Cobern-Browne

Payment: Cks-MC-Visa
Retail: Yes
Designer Discount: 15% off
  $25 or 20% off $50
Classes: Call for schedule
Restringing: Call for quote
Custom Work: Call for quote

Located in historic, downtown Glendale, this unique store occupies an
old craftsman-style bungalow filled with a varied selection of old and
new beads, and related products. Ask about Beadventure Gatherings
(weekend bead retreats in the mountains) three times a year.

BEADS GALORE

2123 S. Priest #201
Tempe, AZ 85282
Phone: 602-921-3949 /800-424-9577
FAX: 602-921-7549
Hours: Mon-Fri 9-6 Sat 9-5 Sun 9-4
Owner: Norman Lawitz

Payment: Cks-MC-Visa
Wholesale: Yes
Mail Order: $30 minimum
Catalog: $10

A large selection of beads from all over the world. Semiprecious stones, Italian and Indian glass, turquoise, African trade beads, pearls, seed and bugle beads, charms, fetishes, pendants, and a wide assortment of findings, bead supplies and books.

BEADBOX, INC.

10135 E. Via Linda
Scottsdale, AZ 85258
Phone: 602-451-4563 /800-232-3279
FAX: 602-451-1014
Hours: Mon-Sat 9-5:30
Owners: Stephanie and Herbert Budwig

Payment: Cks-MC-Visa
Retail: Yes
Wholesale: $250 minimum
Mail Order: $20 minimum
Catalog: $5
Classes: Call for schedule

This retail store carries all of the beads, jewelry, kits, tools and findings shown in the full color catalog as well as an ever-changing variety of the latest trends in beads, jewelry and books.

BEAUCOUP BEADS LIMITED

6538B East Tanque Verde Road
Tucson, AZ 85715
Phone: 602-290-6300
FAX: 602-885-7950
Hours: By appointment only
Owners: Nancy Ferguson and David Smith
Specialty: Czech glass
Exhibiting at: Tucson Gem Show

Payment: Cks-MC-Visa
Wholesale: Yes
Mail Order: Yes

Traveling sales rep who sells to bead and craft stores with a showroom open by appointment.

Bugle beads are tubular-shaped beads which can be round, faceted or twisted.

BE-JEWELED BY MARY

5310 East Camelback Road
Phoenix, AZ 85018
Phone: 602-840-0024
Hours: By appointment only
Owner: Mary Sherrill
Specialty: Old Czech beads

Payment: Cks-MC-Visa-Disc.
Retail: Yes
Mail Order: $25 minimum
Classes: By appointment
Restringing: Yes
Custom Work: Call for prices
Finished Pieces: Yes

Exhibiting at: many gem and mineral shows. Call for schedule.

Beads from all over the world. Mary also redesigns old jewelry pieces and teaches beadwork.

BLACK STAR TRADING CO.

P.O. Box 22511
Flagstaff, AZ 86002
Phone: 602-526-2671
FAX: 602-526-5609
Hours: Mon-Fri 9-5
Owner: Anne Mottek Lucas

Payment: Cks-MC-Visa
Wholesale: $50 minimum
Mail Order: $50 minimum
Catalog: Yes
Finished Pieces: Yes

Specialty: Indian imports, gems and jewelry
Exhibiting at: Tucson Gem and Mineral Show

Wholesaler and direct importer of fine gems and jewelry. Specializing in handmade Mogul silver beads and jewelry; faceted and cabochon gemstones (calibrated, fancy cuts, bullets and opposed bar cuts); precious bead necklaces (emerald, ruby, sapphire); ready-to-wear fancy garnet necklaces. New line of jewelry of sterling and 80% silver beads adorned with stained glass.

BOVIS BEAD CO.

P. O. Box 13345
4500 E. Speedway Blvd. #67
Tucson, AZ 85732
Phone/FAX: 602-318-9512
Hours: Mon-Sat 10-4
Owner: Pierre G. Bovis
Specialty: French glass beads

Payment: Cks-MC-Visa-AE
Wholesale: $100 minimum
Mail Order: $100 minimum
Catalog: $10

Distributor of the famous French glass seed beads. Crow and pony beads, old time colors, and complete selection of colors and sizes of white hearts. Also tube, stripe and many types of glass and silver.

COCOPAH JEWELRY CO.

P. O. Box 1200
Tlaquepaque #C101
Sedona, AZ 86339
Phone: 602-282-4928
FAX: 602-282-6404
Hours: Daily 10-5
Owner: Ann Fabricant

Payment: Cks-MC-Visa
Retail: Yes
Wholesale: $50 minimum
Catalog: $3 refundable
Classes: Call for schedule
Restringing: Yes
Custom Work: Call for quote
Finished Pieces: Yes

One of the oldest bead stores in America, it started in Woodstock, NY in 1970. The collection reflects many years of investment and includes hard to find items focusing on collectibles. No seed beads or Czech because Ann believes that the new bead stores are heavily stocked with those beads and she plans to outlast the craze by focusing on rare and more collectible beads. Also unique one-of-a-kind bead kits.

THE COPPER COYOTE

9430 E. Golf Links #286
Tucson, AZ 85730
Phone: 602-722-8440
FAX: 602-886-5214
Hours: By appointment only
Owner: Gwenn and Steven Yaple
Specialty: Japanese seed beads
Exhibiting at: Tucson Bead Society bazaars.

Payment: Cks-MC-Visa
Retail: Yes
Wholesale: Yes
Price List: SASE
Mail Order: Yes
Custom Work: Call for quote
Finished Pieces: Yes

Importers of Japanese seed beads. These award-winning bead artists have designed and published the unique "Bead Design Graph Paper". They offer the highest quality products and friendly personalized service, and edit the Tucson Bead Society newsletter.

DOUBLE JOY BEADS

7121 E. Sahuaro Drive
Scottsdale, AZ 85254
Phone: 602-994-4495
FAX: 602-443-9540
Hours: By appointment only
Owner: Pat Knight
Specialty: Copper beads, old glass
Exhibiting at: Arizona Bead Society bazaars

Payment: Cks-MC-Visa
Retail: Yes
Wholesale: $100 minimum
Catalog: Copper beads
Classes: Call for information
Restringing: Yes
Custom Work: Call for quote
Finished Pieces: Yes

One of the best-kept secrets in the Valley and the largest collection of rare, unusual and copper beads. Flexible hours for busy beaders and out of town visitors. Unique beads and findings for all your projects. Pat travels the world to bring unique beads to her customers.

DREAM WEAVER BEADS

PO Box 1517
74 Main Street
Bisbee, AZ 85603
Phone: 602-432-4237
Hours: Mon 10-5 Tues, Wed
  & Fri 12-5, Thurs 9:30-1:30
  Sat-Sun 10-6
Owner: Bonnie Hayford

Payment: Cks-MC-Visa
Retail: Yes
Catalog: In process
Classes: Individual instruction
Restringing: Yes
Custom Work: Call for quote
Finished Pieces: Yes

A new little bead shop with a big heart and big dreams. A collection of special beads, Native American beadwork , unique treasures, local artisan made handblown glass, sterling and ceramic beads. Personalized service and the staff will search for your special needs. A good selection of seed beads and a continually expanding line.

HARDIES

P. O. Box 1920
15891 Main Street, Bus Loop I-10
(Across from McDonalds)
Quartzsite, AZ 85346
Phone: 602-927-6381, 800-962-2775
FAX: 602-927-4814
Hours: Mon-Sun 8-5
Owners: Ken and Alice Hardies

Payment: Cks-MC-Visa-Disc.
Retail: Yes
Wholesale: Yes
Mail Order: $60 minimum
Catalog: $3 or free with
  resale number

Quartzsite is in the very heart of the Sonora Desert and is home of the largest Gem, Mineral and Bead show in the world. Hardies is unique. Retail they sell Indian jewelry, Black Hills gold, gemstone jewelry, beaded necklaces, earrings, and all kinds of beads and books. They wholesale Czech glass beads of all sizes, shapes and colors, glass beads from many other countries, metal and metal plated beads, semiprecious, cabochons and many more beads. The findings department sells supplies for any project.

JAC JAN BEADS, ETC.

251 Hwy. 179 #A-3
Sedona, AZ 86336
Phone: 602-282-6780
Hours: Mon 10-5 Wed-Sat 10-5 Sun 12-5
Owner: Jacque and William Brand
Specialty: Collector beads

Payment: Cks-MC-Visa
Retail: Yes
Mail Order: Yes
Classes: Call for information

All kinds of beads from around the world, collector beads and jewelry, collectibles and folk art.

KIVA ARTS

P. O. Box 1430
909 N. Main Street
Cottonwood, AZ 86326
Phone: 602-634-3946
Hours: Call first, Tues-Thurs 10-4
Owner: Kia Frender
Specialty: Huichol Indian beadwork only.

Payment: Cks-MC-Visa
Retail: Yes
Wholesale: Yes
Mail Order: Yes
Catalog: Free brochure
Custom Work: Specialty repair

Located in the Verde Valley near Sedona, Kia sells the unique beadwork of the Huichol Indians including original yarn paintings, other tribal handcrafts, drums and pottery.

PINEY HOLLOW

427 N. 4th Avenue
Tucson, AZ 85705
Phone: 602-623-4450
Hours: Mon-Fri 10-6
  Sat 10-5:30 Sun 12-4
Owners: Michael & Mimi Haggerty

Payment: Cks-MC-Visa-AE
Retail: Yes
Classes: Call for schedule
Restringing: Call for quote
Custom Work: Yes
Finished Pieces: Yes
Consignment: Call

A friendly and helpful atmosphere with assistance provided in designing and assembling your ideas or they will help design a piece of jewelry to be custom-made by them. The bead selection is from around the world. New! A time line bead gallery displaying an old collection of beads from around the world.

SCOTTSDALE BEAD SUPPLY

3625 N. Marshall Way
Scottsdale, AZ 85251
Phone: 602-945-5988
FAX: 602-945-4248
Hours: Mon-Sat 9:30-5
Owners: Michael & Kelly Charveaux
Specialty: Handmade beads
Exhibiting at: the Tucson and Arizona Bead Bazaars.

Payment: Cks-MC-Visa-AE
Retail: Yes
Wholesale: Yes
Classes: Call for schedule
Finished Pieces: Yes

A wholesale and retail bead supply store featuring glass and stone beads from every corner of the world. A full line of findings and supplies, Bali silver beads, unusual findings and books.

SEDONA BEADS

P. O. Box 3434
West Sedona, AZ 86340
1575 West Highway 89A
Sedona, AZ 86336
Phone: 602-282-5880
FAX: 602-282-2464
Hours: Mon-Sat 10-5
Owner: Heather Hakola-Walters
Specialty: Japanese seed beads

Payment: Cks-MC-Visa
Retail: Yes
Wholesale: $250 minimum
Mail Order: Yes
Designer Discount: 25%
Catalog: $5
Classes: Call for schedule
Custom Work: Yes
Finished Pieces: Yes
Gallery Space: Yes

Surrounded by ancient ruins and mystical red rocks, Sedona Beads has over 300 colors of seed beads, custom moccasins, jewelry and garments, art supplies, leather, findings, cabochons, ethnic, glass and gemstone beads. Treasures that translate your imagination into style.

SHOOTING STARR GALLERY OF BEADS

P. O. Box 2719
Fort Verde Plaza #2719
Camp Verde, AZ 86322
Phone: 602-567-4015
Hours: Mon-Thurs 10-5
 Fri 10:30-5:30 Sat 10-5
Owner: Sadie Starr
Specialty: Czech and Japanese

Payment: Cks-MC-Visa
Retail: Yes
Wholesale: $100 minimum
Mail Order: $50 minimum
Catalog: Yes
Classes: Seasonal, call
Finished Pieces: Call
Gallery: Call for details

Sadie Starr is author of the book *Beading with Seed Beads, Gem Stones & Cabochons*. The bead gallery features all kinds of beads from around the world, findings and books.

TOMBSTONE BEAD CO. & TURQUOISE MARKET

P.O. Box 219
416 A Allen Street
Tombstone, AZ 85638
Phone: 602-457-2303
FAX: 602-318-9512
Hours: Mon-Sat 10-5 Sun 12-5
Owner: Shirley Bovis
Specialty: French beads

Payment: Cks-MC-Visa-AE
Retail: Yes
Wholesale: Yes
Mail Order: Yes
Catalog: $10 for three
Classes: Call for schedule
Custom Work: Yes
Finished Pieces: Yes

Bovis French glass seed beads and their famous old time colors and white hearts. Extensive line of Native American craft items, wholesale turquoise, coral and amber beads, Navajo sterling silver beads and clasps and Zuni handcarved fetishes. Ethnic beads, coins and adornments from around the world (antique and contemporary), and much more. **Discount coupon in the back of the Directory.**

UPTOWN TRIBAL

P. O. Box 1803
15B Main Street, Peddler's Alley
Old Bisbee, AZ 85603
Phone: 602-432-4675
FAX: 602-432-7117
Hours: Tues-Sun 10-6 Sat 10-5:30 Sun 12-4
Owner: Kate Drew-Wilkinson
Specialty: Kate's designs

Payment: Cks-MC-Visa-AE
Retail: Yes

Small personal bead gallery selling Kate's own lampworked beads (made with recycled glass) and her unique jewelry designs. Bisbee is an old mining town that has become a thriving artists' community. Kate, a designer for the Nature Company for eight years, is always on hand to help. Visit the gallery to study design ideas in action and to buy great beads.

VENETIAN TRADERS

430 E. Drachman Street
Tucson, AZ 85705
Phone: 602-622-4046
Hours: Call for appointment
Owner: Michael Rollins
Specialty: Venetian glass beads
Exhibiting at: Tucson Gem & Mineral Show in February

Payment: Cks-M.O.
Wholesale: $75 minimum
Mail Order: $75 minimum
Samples: Samples sent satisfaction guaranteed
No catalog

Wholesaler of quality Venetian glass beads. Supplying bead stores and designers with a large selection of beautiful handmade beads personally selected on frequent trips to Venice, Italy. Michael shares his thorough knowledge of the glass industry with his clients.

WISHBONE'S ANTIQUE TRADING POST

P. O. Box 208
Mayer, AZ 86333-0208
Phone: 602-632-4332
Hours: Mon-Sun 9-6:30
Owner: David Albins
Specialty: Old trade beads
Exhibiting at: Arizona Bead Society Bead Bazaars, Spring and Fall.

Payment: Cks-MC-Visa-AE
Retail: Yes
Wholesale: Call for minimum
Mail Order: Call for minimum

Located halfway between Phoenix and Flagstaff, 8 miles west of I-17. This is a working trading post with an array of antiques, collectibles and imports, old trade beads, African, millefiore, Russian blue, old white hearts, green hearts and Native American crafts and baskets.

ARKANSAS

SOUTHWESTERN CREATIONS & BEADS

P. O. Box 265
5640 Batesville Boulevard
Pleasant Plains, AR 72568
Phone: 501-345-2243
Hours: Sat 10-5 /Call first
  Other hours by appointment
Owners: Ali Christman

Payment: Cks
Retail: Yes
Wholesale: Jewelry
Restringing: Yes
Custom Work: Call
Finished Pieces: Yes
Specialty: Porcupine quill jewelry

Small one owner shop. All types of finished beadwork, especially peyote and porcupine quill, primitive treasure necklaces and turquoise and liquid silver jewelry made by the owner. Many kinds of Indian decor, seed beads, chevrons, copper beads and glass 3-cut.

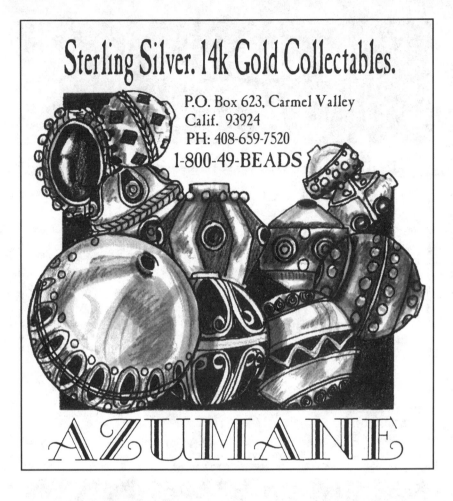

12 California

JULIET ANDERSON

Marin City Flea Market
California Bead Bazaars
Phone: 510-451-6451
Hours: By appointment
Specialty: Ethnic and glass beads

Payment: Cks
Retail: Yes
Wholesale: Yes

Juliet sells a unique variety of ethnic and glass beads at the flea market and the Northern California and Los Angeles bead bazaars.

ARTISTRY WITH BEADS

3008 W. Burbank Blvd.
Burbank, CA 91505
Phone: 818-848-1782
FAX: 818-848-2002

Payment: Cks-MC-Visa
Retail: Yes
Wholesale: $20 min. 1st time
Mail Order: Yes
Catalog: Call for price

Hours: Mon, Sat 10-6 Tues-Fri 10-8 **Classes:** Call for schedule
Owners: Orlando Bevington and John C. Heinrich
Specialty: Ethnic and handmade beads

Incredible selection of thousands of beads from all over the world. Friendly, helpful staff, fine jewelry repair, plating service available, earring kits, gift boxes, findings, and wire. Special orders available.

ASCONA BEADS

1940 14th Street
Santa Monica, CA 90404
Phone: 310-450-8939
Hours: Mon-Sat 10-5
Contact: Barbara or Ricki
Specialty: Glass beads

Payment: Cks-MC-Visa
Retail: Yes
Wholesale: Yes
Mail Order: Yes
Classes: Call for schedule

All kinds of beads, books and findings. You'll find beads on all the walls and tables. New, expanded class schedule.

White-heart bead. A bead made with two layers of glass fused one over the other. The outer layer, a transparent colored glass, covers an opaque core, usually white. *The New Beadwork*, Kathlyn Moss and Alice Scherer.

AZUMANE

P. O. Box 623
Carmel Valley, CA 93924
Phone: 408-659-7520, 800-492-3237
Hours: By appointment only
Owners: Amanda Kerfoot, Azul Amey
Specialty: Precious metal beads
Exhibiting at many Gem Faires and bead bazaars, call for schedule.

Payment: Cks-MC-Visa
Retail: Yes
Wholesale: $100 minimum
Mail Order: Yes
Catalog: Call

Finished Pieces: Yes

Bala Imports and Gyre & Gimbel beads joined together to create Azumane. Their goal is to carry the widest selection of unusual components, findings and beads possible. They carry hundreds of styles of sterling silver beads and are adding both antique and contemporary 24K gold beads this year. They have orissa brass and other tribal brass, Tibetan turquoise, amber, carnelian and collectables. Great selection of rare, one-of-a-kind pieces, jewelry and lots more.

BARBETTA'S BEADS

2316 J Street
Sacramento, CA 95816
Phone: 916-443-4959
Hours: Mon-Sat 11-6 Sun 11-4
Owner: Barbetta Lockart
Specialty: Special pieces
Exhibiting at: Northern California Bead Society bazaars and the River City Quilters Guild Quilt Show

Payment: Cks-MC-Visa-AE
Retail: Yes
Wholesale: $25 minimum
Discount: Yes
Classes: Call for information
Consignment: Call for details
Gallery: Call for details

A great bead store offering the gamut of bead choices from new and antique, glass to ceramic to metals and many others. A complete offering of findings, jewelry supplies, books, ethnographic items and art pieces by artisans from all over the US. Workspace is available for customers. A must-see experience, known for unusual special pieces many of museum quality. The best bead store in Sacramento.

Bead History: In Ban Kwow, a village near Thailand's border with Kampuchea, the ancient art of crafting beads from silver and gold is flourishing. These beads are interesting not only for their beauty, but also for their mode of manufacture and the significance of their shapes and designs. Their manufacture involves creating beads from thin strips of pure silver, filling the insides with lac, a tree resin, for strength and then engraving and chasing the designs by hands. Their shapes and designs are inextricably bound to the Thai and Khmer religious court and village traditions from which they rose. *An Ancient Khmer Beadmaking Art in Modern Thailand*, Duangporn and Steven Dunning.

BAUBLES & BEADS

1676 Shattuck Avenue
Berkeley, CA 94709
Phone: 510-644-2323
FAX: 510-644-2328
Hours: Mon-Sat 11-6 Sun 12-5
Owners: Jim and Lisa Kaufman
Specialty: Unique selection

Payment: Cks-MC-Visa
Retail: Yes
Wholesale: $25 minimum
Discount: 20% w/resale no.
Classes: Call for schedule
Restringing: Yes

Exhibiting at: Northern California Bead Society Bazaar

Newly expanded into a spacious new store in the heart of Berkeley.
Wide selection of beads from around the world. Friendly staff to
assist with questions on design and construction. Workspace available. Also tools, findings and a great selection of books, charms and
stringing supplies. **Discount coupon in the back of the Directory.**

BEAD BAZAAR

3059-K Hopyard Road/Hopyard Vlg.
Pleasanton, CA 94566
Phone: 510-484-5320
Hours: Mon-Sat 11-6:30 Sun 12-5:30
Owner: Joan Wedemeyer
Specialty: Wide variety

Payment: Cks-MC-Visa
Retail: Yes
Wholesale: $50 minimum
Classes: Call for information
Gallery: Yes
Consignment: Yes
Finished Pieces: Yes

Exhibiting at: Northern California Bead Society bead bazaars.

This spacious store features tables full of beads well organized by
colors with one table devoted to all the new arrivals. Lots of vintage
beads and buttons; unique pendants and other jewelry components;
both Japanese and Czech seed beads; books, tools, kits and all kinds
of beading supplies. Work space and assistance is always available.

THE BEAD BOUTIQUE

4187 Campus Drive M172
Irvine, CA 92715
Phone: 714-725-0468
FAX: 714-786-7081
Hours: Mon-Sat 11-8 Sun 12-5
Specialty: Wide variety
Owner: Patricia Abahusayn

Payment: Cks-MC-Visa
Retail: Yes
Finished Pieces: Yes
Gallery Space: Yes
Restringing: Call for quote

Everything from a children's table of inexpensive beads to semiprecious and antique pieces and a work table for customers to work
and receive free help. Complete line of findings, glass, wood, plated,
sterling and 14K gold-filled beads. Also tools, books and accessories
and a large selection of finished jewelry from ethnic to contemporary
at great prices. Children's parties a specialty.

BEAD BOX

309 N. Kings Road
Los Angeles, CA 90048
Phone: 213-651-3595
Hours: Mon-Tues-Thurs 10-6
  Wed, Fri 10-7 Sat 10-4 Sun 12-5
Owner: Suzy Zlotnick
Specialty: Beading on clothing

Payment: Cks-MC-Visa-AE
Retail: Yes
Wholesale: $25 minimum
Mail Order: $25 minimum
Catalog: $3

Beading for clothing and jewelry. Wide variety of beads, sew-on stones, fringes and trims. They work with each customer to meet their individual needs and have worked with professionals such as designers, costumers and dancers since 1950.

BEAD BUNGALOW

1776 Churn Creek Road
Redding, CA 96002
Phone: 916-223-3999
Hours: Mon-Sat 9:30-5:30
Owners: Kathy and Ron Dickey
Specialty: Handmade beads

Payment: Cks-MC-Visa
Retail: Yes
Wholesale: $100 minimum
Classes: Call for information
Restringing: Yes
Custom Work: Call for prices
Finished Pieces: Yes
Gallery Space: Yes

Their slogan is "a special place to bead." Antique lace curtains and handmade quilts hanging from the cozy loft create a warm and friendly atmosphere to escape to and enjoy beading. Work table with free use of tools and instruction sheets. Staff is always available to answer questions and offer assistance. A full range of beads including seed, African trade, clay, Czech, glass, Fimo and handmade beads.

THE BEAD FETISH

801 D Street
San Rafael, CA 94901
Phone: 415-457-8891
Hours: Mon-Wed 10-6 Thurs 10-8
    Fri 10-6 Sat 10-5 Sun 11-5
Owners: Kim and Scott Fandry
Specialty: Service and variety

Payment: Cks-MC-Visa-AE
Retail: Yes
Wholesale: $35 minimum
Mail Order: $25 minimum
Classes: Call for schedule
Restringing: Yes
Custom Work: Call for prices

Kim and Scott opened the store in 1990 out of their love for beads and a long time dream of opening a bead store. The business has grown steadily over the years and they are always adding new beads. They offer an exciting and extensive schedule of classes for kids, teens and adults and "all you can make" jewelry and Fimo parties. Huge variety of beads, tools, books, leather, supplies, looms, and a helpful staff. Next time you're in the San Francisco Bay area come see for yourself.

THE BEAD GALLERY

328 Oak Street
Red Bluff, CA 96080
Phone: 916-527-9105
FAX: 916-529-0977
Hours: Tues -Sat 10-5:30
    Mon and Sun by appt. only
Owners: Susan Clarke and
    Randy Moller
Specialty: Wide variety

Payment: Cks-MC-Visa
Retail: Yes
Wholesale: $50 min-20% off
Mail Order: Yes
Classes: Call for information
Restringing: Yes
Custom Work: Call for prices
Finished Pieces: Yes
Gallery Space: Yes

Susan Clarke, a successful jewelry designer and manufacturer for over 10 years has converted an art gallery into a bead shop. A large selection of beads and findings at great prices for the serious beader or jewelry designer. All colors and sizes of seed beads to size 24°, delicas, Swarovski crystal, cabochons, rhinestones, Czech glass, gemstones, antique, ethnic, Fimo and many findings and books.

BEAD GALLERY

1809 Manhattan Beach Boulevard
Manhattan Beach, CA 90266
Phone: 310-372-3136
FAX: 310-372-5948
Hours: Mon-Sat 10-6:30
Owner: Isaac Younai
Specialty: Beads, rhinestones

Payment: Cks
Retail: Yes
Wholesale: $25 minimum
Catalog: Yes
Classes: Call for schedule
Restringing: Yes
Custom Work: Call for prices
Finished Pieces: Yes

Craft supplies, findings and rhinestones and a wide selection of ready to-wear earrings and accessories. Many kinds of craft supplies.

BEAD IT

1325 Pacific Avenue
Santa Cruz, CA 95060
Phone: 408-426-0779
FAX: 408-429-6919
Hours: Mon-Sat 10-6 Sun 11-6
Owner: Sue Nelson

Payment: Cks-MC-Visa-AE
Retail: Yes
Mail Order: $20 minimum
Restringing: Yes
Finished Pieces: Yes
Specialty: Great service

In Santa Cruz since 1987 with a huge selection of beads. The staff is always happy to help assemble or advise you on your beading needs.

BEAD MANIA

100 N. Glendora Ave. #108
Glendora, CA 91741
Phone: 818-852-9770
Hours: Mon-Wed 10-5:30
    Thurs-Sat 10-6 Sun 12-3
Owner: Lois Thompson
Specialty: Semiprecious and Czech glass beads

Payment: Cks-MC-Visa
Retail: Yes
Restringing: Yes
Finished Pieces: Yes
Consignment: Only during
    Christmas season

Jewelry-making tools, books, supplies and a large variety of beads sold in a friendly atmosphere. In-store work table with tools and assistance in designing and completing projects in the store. Sterling silver and 14K gold filled beads and findings sold at competitive prices. Group and birthday parties by appointment.

BEAD RANCH

605 Town & Country Village
Sunnyvale, CA 94086
Phone: 408-739-8842
Hours: Mon-Wed 11-6
    Thurs 11-7 Fri 11-6 Sat 10-5
Owners: Susan Terry, Dave Allender
 Nancy Bracewell, Gina Senzatimore
Specialty: Sam & Dave beads!

Payment: Cks-MC-Visa
Retail: Yes
Designer Discount: 20%
    with $30 minimum order
Classes: Call for information
Restringing: Yes
Custom Work: Call for prices
Finished Pieces: Yes
Consignment: Call

Exhibiting at Santa Fe Bead Expo, June 1995, New Mexico and Northern California Bead Society bead bazaars.

The only store where you can buy the wonderful and whimsical handmade Sam & Dave polymer clay beads. A small family-owned bead store selling glass, Japanese seed beads, African trade beads, tools, findings, buttons, stringing supplies and finished jewelry. Always willing to help customers design jewelry and always looking for unusual beads to offer their customers. The jewelry made with the Sam & Dave beads make great gifts. A fun store.

THE BEAD SHACK

4927 Sonoma Hwy., Unit E
Santa Rosa, CA 95405
Phone: 707-539-1858
Hours: Tues-Sat 10-7
Owner: Stan
Specialty: Czech beads

Payment: Cks-MC-Visa
Retail: Yes
Wholesale: $100 minimum
Mail Order: $50 minimum
Classes: Call for information
Finished Pieces: Yes
Restringing: Call for quote

Exhibiting at: various Native American pow wows, call for schedule.

A full service bead and jewelry supply store importing from India, Indonesia and Hong Kong. A wide variety of beads sold in bulk and small packages, semiprecious beads, findings, needles, threads and much more. A friendly staff will help with design, classes, purchases and gift certificates. Over 500 colors of seed and bugle beads.

THE BEAD SHOP

899 South Coast Hwy.
Laguna Beach, CA 92651
Phone: 714-494-2115
Hours: Mon-Sat 10-6 Sun 12-6
Owners: Virginia Mason
  and Analee Dixon
Contact: Susie Milette

Payment: Cks-MC-Visa
Retail: Yes
Wholesale: Quantity discounts
Mail Order: Yes
Classes: Call for schedule
Finished Pieces: Yes
Gallery Space: Yes
Consignment: Yes

Lots of help given to people when buying their beads and assistance given to help make your own jewelry. Large collection of "collector" beads. Every conceivable bead for sale here.

THE BEAD SHOP

177 Hamilton Avenue
Palo Alto, CA 94301
Phone: 415-328-7925
FAX: 415-328-7893
Hours: Mon-Wed 10-6
  Thurs-Fri 10-8 Sat 10-6 Sun 12-5
Owner: Janice Parsons
Specialty: Free design consultation

Payment: Cks-MC-Visa-Discover
Retail: Yes
Wholesale: $100 minimum
Mail Order: Yes
Classes: Call for schedule
Restringing: Yes
Custom Work: Call for quote
Finished Pieces: Yes

Exhibiting at: the San Mateo Gem & Mineral Shows, Fall, Winter, Spring. Call for exact dates.

The third oldest bead store in Northern California located in downtown Palo Alto near Stanford University (close to restaurants and shops), is always busy. Come with a friend, bring a project and plan to spend the day. All kinds of beads, Czech, German glass, metal, charms, ceramics, findings, and Don't Worry Bead Happy t-shirts and many unusual beads and things.

THE BEAD SHOP

201 First Street
Los Altos, CA 94022
Phone: 415-949-1984
FAX: 415-949-2718
Hours: Mon-Sat 10-6 Sun 12-5
Owner: Janice Parsons
Contact: Karen Barry, Mgr.
Specialty: Free design consultation

Payment: Cks-MC-Visa
Retail: Yes
Wholesale: $100 minimum
Mail Order: Yes
Classes: Call for schedule
Restringing: Yes
Custom Work: Call for quote
Finished Pieces: Yes

Exhibiting at: the San Mateo Gem & Mineral Shows, Fall, Winter, Spring. Call for exact dates.

Located in the Village of Los Altos and home to many of The Bead Shop's classes. An ideal place to get your creativity flowing. Like the other Bead Shop stores, the Los Altos store is bright and well organizedwith plenty of room to work and an experienced staff ready to help. The entire range from seed beads and Fimo to Indonesian silver, beading tools, charms, findings and books.

THE BEAD SHOP

605 Town & Country Village
Stevens Creek at Winchester Blvd.
San Jose, CA 95128
Phone: 408-261-0432
FAX: 408-246-4037
Hours: Mon-Sat 10-6 Sun 12-5
Owner: Janice Parsons
Contact: Kim Anderson, Mgr.
Specialty: Classes and bead parties

Payment: Cks-MC-Visa-Discover
Retail: Yes
Wholesale: $100 minimum
Mail Order: Yes
Classes: Call for schedule
Restringing: Yes
Custom Work: Call for quote
Finished Pieces: Yes

Exhibiting at: the San Mateo Gem & Mineral Shows, Fall, Winter, Spring. Call for exact dates.

Conveniently located off Highways 880 and 280, this new store has a wonderful work area and lots of open space. Ample free parking makes this Bead Shop the perfect location for special event Trunk Shows. The widest assortment of first quality beads, tools, books and findings. Tools, looms, wire, design boards and whatever you need to complete your project. Come in on your birthday and with proof of birth date, beads are 30% off. They also honor other bead store coupons.

BEAD STATION

31761 Camino Capistrano
San Juan Capistrano, CA
Phone: 714-661-2323
Hours: Mon-Sat 10-5   Sun 11-5
Owners: Linda Mondt and Ann Plantenberg

Payment: Cks-MC-Visa-Discover
Retail: Yes
Wholesale: $100 minimum
Mail Order: Yes
Finished Pieces: Yes

A great selection of all kinds of beads and findings. Friendly, helpful staff to assist in making the right choices.

BEAD STATION

24412 Muirlands Blvd. #A
Lake Forest, CA 92630
Phone: 714-859-2323
FAX: 714-859-2323
Hours: Mon-Sat 10-5
Owners: Linda Mondt and Ann Plantenberg

Payment: Cks-MC-Visa-Discover
Retail: Yes
Wholesale: $100 minimum
Mail Order: Yes
Finished Pieces: Yes

A great selection of all kinds of beads and findings. Friendly, helpful staff will help in design choices.

THE BEAD STORE

73-382 El Paseo
Palm Desert, CA 92260
Phone: 619-341-9559
FAX: 619-346-9508
Hours: Mon-Sat 10-5
Owner: Heide Karre
Specialty: Custom jewelry design

Payment: Cks-MC-Visa
Retail: Yes
Wholesale: $100 minimum
Mail Order: $15 minimum
Classes: Call for information
Restringing: Yes
Custom Work: Call for pricing
Finished Pieces: Call for quote

The only full-line bead store in the desert. Over 5,000 different beads from all over the world, quality tools, findings and books. One stop for all your beading needs. Large selection of designer buttons, rhinestones, beaded fringes and trims. One-of-a-kind finished jewelry designs and always something new and unusual.

BEAD WERK

10895 Pico Boulevard
Los Angeles, CA 90064
Phone: 310-470-1515
FAX: 310-470-7116
Hours: Mon-Fri 12-6 Sat 10-6
Owner: Tzerl Seltzer

Payment: Cks-MC-Visa
Retail: Yes
Wholesale: $25 minimum
Mail Order: $25 minimum
Restringing: Yes
Custom Work: $25 minimum
Finished Pieces: Call for quote

A broad range of the finest materials and goods, backed by expert professional advice, allows all customers to choose just what they need for their special designs. The owner's extensive contacts can source special requests. Highest quality imported and domestic beads, findings, old and new beads, artifacts, antiques and many books.

THE BEADED BEAR

Box 9249-1204
San Jose, CA 95157
Phone: 408-379-8647
Hours: By appointment only
Owner: Sigrid Wynne-Evans
Specialty: Unique designs

Payment: Cks
Retail: Yes
Wholesale: Yes
Mail Order: Yes
Product List: $1 and SASE
Classes: See information below
Restringing: Call for prices
Custom Work: Call for quote
Finished Pieces: Yes

Author of the book, *Earrings Designs By Sig,* featuring unique earring patterns exclusively by Sig. Sig sells finished pieces: earrings, bracelets, medicine bags, necklaces, beaded ritual items and dream/sun catchers. Classes on all the above and more cost $25 per class if there is more than one person in class or $40 for private lessons.

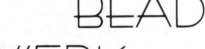

THE BEADED NOMAD

1122 First Street
Napa, CA 94559
Phone: 707-258-8004
Hours: Mon-Sat 11-6 Sun 12-5
Owner: Peggy Owens Erridge
Specialty: Unusual beads

Payment: Cks-MC-Visa
Retail: Yes
Wholesale: $50 minimum
Classes: Call for information
Restringing: Yes
Finished Pieces: Call for quote

Come and peruse a plethora of fine beads and baubles from around the world. The largest selection of beads in Napa County with a friendly and knowledgeable staff to assist you. Glass, Fimo, ceramic, semiprecious and vintage beads and ethnographic pieces from Asia, India and Africa.

THE BEADMAN

2425 Athens Avenue
Redding, CA 96001
Phone: 916-243-8808
FAX: 916-243-4029
Hours: Mon-Sat 10-6 Sun 12-5
Owner: Sandra Arbo
Specialty: Glass beads

Payment: Cks-MC-Visa-AE-ATM
Retail: Yes
Wholesale: $25 minimum
Mail Order: $25 minimum
Restringing: Yes

A full service bead store carrying findings, all types of beads and macrame supplies. The Beadman is a throwback to the '60s. Unique combination of the old-type head shop and contemporary crafts store.

BEADS

911-1/2 State Street
Santa Barbara, CA 93101
Phone: 805-966-1138
FAX: 805-966-3175
Hours: Mon-Thurs 10-6
    Fri-Sat 10-8 Sun 12-5
Owners: Barbara and Lee Nelson
Specialty: Ethnic and Czech glass beads

Payment: Cks-MC-Visa
Retail: Yes
Wholesale: $20 minimum
Mail Order: $20 minimum
Finished Pieces: Yes

Other Location: Pismo Beach
    187 Pomeroy Ave., 773-0621

A world class bead shop in the heart of Santa Barbara with the very best in beads and beadcraft supplies for the collector and the beginner. The prices and selection reflect years of working with manufacturers to make the designs and colors their customers ask for. A wide variety of gemstone beads, sterling, glass, seed, crystal, cloisonne, charms, and Peruvian and African beads. Cultural and ethnic jewelry from all over the world. **Mention The Bead Directory for a 10% discount.**

BEADS, BASKETS & MEMORIES

324 Suite L Oak Street
Bakersfield, CA 93304
Phone: 805-321-9798
Hours: Tues-Fri 9-5 Sat 9-4 Sun 9-3
Owners: Valerie Campise and
  Pat Milton
Specialty: Customer service

Payment: Cks
Retail: Yes
Discount: 10% to designers
Mail Order: Yes
Classes: Individual instruction
Finished Pieces: Yes
Consignment: Call

A mother and daughter team creates a tranquil and friendly beading environment. A wide variety of beads and findings to inspire the beginner and the professional designer. In-store workspace available, and assistance in design and assembly of your creations. Large variety of glass, gemstone, sterling silver, and antique trade beads.

Beads

9111/2 State Street
SANTA BARBARA, CA 93101
(805) 966-1138
FAX (805) 966-3175
MON - THURS 10-6
FRI - SAT 10-8 • SUN - 12-5

187 Pomeroy
PISMO BEACH, CA
93449
(805) 773-0621
MON - SAT 10-6
SUN - 10-5

Since 1984 **Beads** has been a <u>MUST STOP</u> for beaders from the novice to the professional artist. This year we are celebrating our 10th Anniversary at our beautiful, new, larger store in Santa Barbara. Our specialties include Czech Glass, Sterling Silver, Ethnic, Charms & Fimo. **Beads** sells retail and wholesale with quantity discounts for all.

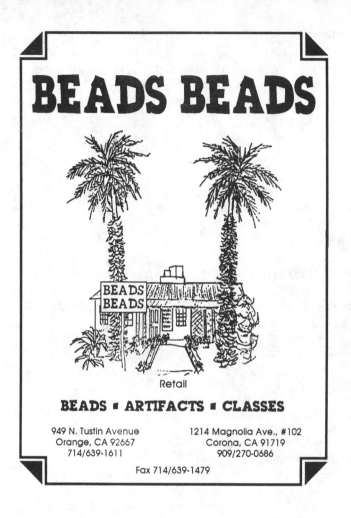

BEADS BEADS

949 N. Tustin Avenue
Orange, CA 92667
Phone: 714-639-1611
FAX: 714-639-1479
Hours: Mon-Sat 10-6
Specialty: Ethnic
Owners: Lori Holman and
  Chuck Paddock

Payment: Cks-MC-Visa-Disc.
Retail: Yes
Wholesale: Discount
Mail Order: Yes
Catalog: $2
Free Catalog w/Resale #: Yes
Restringing: Yes
Custom Work: Call for prices
Finished Pieces: Yes

A friendly, helpful bead store with free instruction and three rooms
full of beads from around the world. African and Native American
trade beads and artifacts and turquoise pawn jewelry.

BEADS BEADS

1214 Magnolia Avenue #102
Corona, CA 91719
Phone: 909-270-0686
Hours: Mon-Fri 11-7 Sat 10-6
Specialty: Ethnic
Owners: Lori Holman and
Chuck Paddock

Payment: Cks-MC-Visa-Disc.
Retail: Yes
Wholesale: Discount
Mail Order: Yes
Catalog: $2 or free with
resale number
Classes: Call for schedule
Restringing: Yes
Custom Work: Call for prices

Beads and artifacts from around the world. A friendly, helpful staff
will help design and complete your project. Extensive class schedule.
Native American and African artifacts, books, buttons, trade beads.
turquoise pawn jewelry and tools.

BEADS BY THE BAY

865 Main Street
Morro Bay, CA 93442
Phone: 805-772-5403
Hours: Mon-Sat 10-5
Closed Tues. Sun 11-4
Owner: Maggie and Karl Presser
Specialty: Gemstone beads

Payment: Cks-MC-Visa
Retail: Yes
Classes: Call for schedule
Restringing: Call for quote
Custom Work: Call for quote
Finished Pieces: Yes
Consignment: Call for details
Gallery Space: Call for details

Full service bead store in a small, oceanside community. Over 3,000
different types of beads and charms. Personal attention and
assistance with completion of your project. Unique beads, old, new,
seed, African trade, glass, crystal and supplies. Finished designer
jewelry, sterling silver jewelry, rocks and minerals.

BEADS ETC.

3053 Hwy 50
South Lake Tahoe, CA 96150
Phone: 916-544-1323
Hours: Mon-Thurs 10-6
Fri-Sat 10-7 Sun 10-6
Owner: Steven and Phyllis Palmieri
Specialty: Wide variety

Payment: Cks-MC-Visa
Retail: Yes
Wholesale: Yes
Restringing: Call for quote
Custom Work: Call for quote
Finished Pieces: Yes

A step back in time to the 1960s. A complete selection of beads from
around the world, findings, natural fiber clothing, batik, tie-dye and
embroidery. The owners travel the world looking for interesting
things that blend in with what they sell. Semiprecious, pendants,
sterling silver, African trade beads and a large selection of Indian glass
and metal beads. Second store in Reno, Nevada.

BEADS AND MORE

967 First Street, Ste. 105
Encinitas, CA 92024
Phone: 619-942-5222
FAX: 619-483-0607
Hours: Mon-Sat 10-8 Sun 11-6
Owner: Jaye Dibos
Specialty: Great selection

Payment: Cks-MC-Visa
Retail: Yes
Wholesale: Yes
Mail Order: Yes
Classes: Call for schedule
Finished Pieces: Yes

Beads from all over the world, sterling silver, gold-filled, glass, wood, plated, natural stone. Findings, tools, books and much more.

BEADS AND MORE

4150 Mission Blvd., Ste. 111
San Diego, CA 92109
Phone: 619-483-4190
FAX: 619-483-0607
Hours: Mon-Sat 10-8 Sun 11-6
Owner: Kandra Norsigian

Payment: Cks-MC-Visa
Retail: Yes
Wholesale: Yes
Classes: Call for schedule
Finished Pieces: Yes

Beads from all over the world, sterling silver, gold-filled, glass, wood, plated, natural stone. Findings, tools, books and much more.

BEADS OF MARIN

8 Locust Avenue
Mill Valley, CA 94941
Phone: 415-381-4364
Hours: Mon-Wed 10-6
   Thurs 10-8 Fri-Sat 10-6 Sun 11-4
Owner: Susan Osborne

Payment: Cks-MC-Visa-AE
Retail: Yes
Classes: Call for schedule
Restringing: Yes
Finished Pieces: Yes
Consignment: Call for details
Gallery Space: Call for details

This new bead store has 1,100 sq. ft. of space with a work space for customers. Ongoing classes during store hours. All kinds of beads and the inventory will grow according to customer requests. Beaded accessories on consignment.

MAKING A LOOP

Bend end — Trim end — Start loop — String on and close loop

A   B 3/8" (1cm) C   D

BEADS & ORNAMENTS
5420 Boyd Avenue
Oakland, CA 94618
Phone: 510-655-7559
Hours: By appointment only, no store.
Owner: Golden DeBone
Specialty: Dichroic glass beads and Burkett ojime necklaces
Exhibiting at: Northern California and Los Angeles Bead Society
sales; Himalayan Fair Berkeley, Contemporary Crafts Market, March
'95, San Francisco.

Payment: Cks
Retail: Yes
Finished Pieces: Yes

Glass beadmaker, necklace designer and collector and seller of antique
and ethnic beads. Beads and necklaces are for sale at various bead
bazaars and craft fairs. Golden's necklaces are included in the collections of Whoopi Goldberg and Annie Sprinkle.

BEADS N' THINGS

1033 Pacific Coast Hwy.
Seal Beach, CA 90740
Phone: 310-430-9818
Hours: Mon-Thurs 10-7 Fri 10-9 Sat-Sun 10-6
Owner: Audrey McGavin

Payment: Cks
Retail: Yes
Classes: Call for schedule

A great selection of all kinds of beads from around the world, also findings, and lots of assistance given to help create your own jewelry.

BEADS TO YOU

607 E. Balboa Boulevard
Newport Beach, CA 92661
Phone: 714-675-8960
Hours: Mon-Sat 10-6 Sun 12-6
Owner: Melanie Gargano

Payment: Cks-MC-Visa
Retail: Yes
Mail Order: Yes
Designer Discount: 20% off
  after $25
Finished Pieces: Yes

The staff is always friendly and willing to show you how to design and assemble at no extra charge. A wide selection of beads from around the world. **See Discount Coupon in back of the Directory.**

BEADS UNIQUE

308 Roberts Lane
Bakersfield, CA 93308
Phone: 805-399-6523
FAX: 805-393-7547
Hours: Tues-Sat 10-5
Owners: Peggy Crisman and Shirley Worley

Payment: Cks-MC-Visa
Retail: Yes
Wholesale: Yes
Mail Order: $25 minimum
Catalog: $3
Classes: Call for list

A unique and exciting bead shop filled with lots of beautiful beads, a full selection of findings, tools, books, and bead stringing supplies. Also bead and sequined appliqués, rhinestones, paint and glitter, iron-on and sequins. A fun place to spend the day.

BEADZ

6421 N. Blackstone Avenue
Fresno, CA 93710
Phone: 209-261-2747
FAX: 209-261-0341
Hours: Mon-Sat 10-6 Sun 12-5
Owner: Edy and Tony Ting

Payment: Cks-MC-Visa
Retail: Yes
Wholesale: $100 minimum
Mail Order: $50 minimum
Classes: Call for schedule
Finished Pieces: Yes
Specialty: Workshops

A friendly, comfortable place where good music and helpful people create an enjoyable atmosphere for all beaders. A wide variety of workshops offered by local artists and guest instructors. All kinds of beads, findings, ethnic artifacts, tools, books and stringing supplies.

BELL TOWER BEADS PLUS

434 Main Street /Bead shop
419 Main Street #A/Studio
Placerville, CA 95667
Phone: 916-642-2323
Winter Hours: 11-5:30
Summer Hours: 11-6:30
  Tues by appt only - call 1 week prior
Owner: Lisa Jones and Jeremiah Langley
Specialty: Low prices on unusual designer findings and beads

Payment: Cks-Trade/Barter
Retail: Yes
Wholesale: 10% disc. w/resale
Mail Order: Call first
Classes: Call for schedule
Call Jeremiah for wholesale Fimo
Call Lisa for jewelry and beads

Located in historic downtown Placerville and owned by a mother-son team who have been collecting beads, designing jewelry and selling supplies for 11 years. Low prices on an ever-expanding unique inventory. Also selling their own special jewelry line and exceptional Fimo beads made by Jeremiah. Select the beads and they will create something just for you. Great selection and prices.

BIJOUX FOUS

2315 Spaulding Avenue
Berkeley, CA 94703
Phone: 510-649-7425
Hours: By appointment only
Owner: Melanie Mathias
Specialty: Designer jewelry
Exhibiting at: Northern California Bead Society bazaars.

Payment: Cks
Retail: Yes
Mail Order: Yes
Finished Pieces: Yes

Jewelry designer of handknotted necklaces and bracelets of opals, pearls and lampworked beads. Melanie makes and sells her own glass beads and sells overstock from her jewelry.

THE BLACK BEAD

5003 Newport Avenue
San Diego, CA 92107
Phone: 619-222-2115
Hours: Mon-Sat 10:30-7 Sun 11-6
Owner: Lynn Dornbusch

Payment: Cks-MC-Visa
Retail: Yes
Wholesale: $20 minimum
Restringing: Call
Finished Pieces: Yes

Located less than a block from the ocean in the unique area of Ocean Beach in the city of San Diego. Friendly personal assistance with a large inventory of beads that include seed, bugle, trade, ethnic, Fimo, metal, ceramic, antique glass and novelty beads. A large selection of sterling and base metal charms, findings, tools and books. Huichol Indian masks and artifacts, dream catcher materials and kits.

THE BLACK SHEEP

1010 First Street
Encinitas, CA 92024
Phone: 619-436-9973
Hours: Mon-Sat 10-6 Sun 12-5
Owner: Karen Henderson

Payment: Cks-MC-Visa
Retail: Yes
Classes: Call for schedule
Finished Pieces: Yes

Store may be moving soon, please call to confirm location and hours. A stimulating environment for everyone who loves to knit, weave, crochet or work with beads. They sell antique beads, ethnic, metal, crystal, semiprecious, seed and bugle beads as well as yarns, handwoven accessories, books and exotic earrings.

BROADWAY BEAD

20 Broadway Lane
Walnut Creek, CA 94596
Phone: 510-932-9909
FAX: 707-864-0802
Hours: Mon-Fri 10-9 Sat 10-6
   Sun 11-6
Owner: Karen Hamilton
Contact: Penny Ruhter
Specialty: Classes and repairs

Payment: Cks-MC-Visa
Retail: Yes
Wholesale: $100 minimum
Classes: Call for schedule
Restringing: Call for quote
Custom Work: Call for prices
Finished Pieces: Yes

Customers choose from a large selection of glass beads such as hand blown Czech, Indian, Italian, seed beads, and metal beads from brass to hand carved sterling. All the stringing supplies needed to create and finish your design with the help of the friendly staff at the work table. Also leather, tools, books and storage containers.

BURLEY'S CRAFTS

3739 W. Ramsey Street
Banning, CA 92220
Phone: 909-849-8737
Hours: Mon-Sat 10-5
Owner: Pat Burley

Payment: Cks-MC-Visa
Retail: Yes
Wholesale: $75 minimum

This is a craft-bead shop with a large selection of seed and bugle beads, handmade glass, odd beads and findings and a large selection of craft beads, pony, faceted, pearls etc. A small shop with an inviting atmosphere. Come in and work and exchange ideas and patterns.

BWANACON

1327 1/2 Abbot Kinney Blvd.
Venice, CA 90291
Phone: 310-396-4403
Hours: Mon-Fri 11-5 Sat 10-2 Sun. by appt.
Owner: Stephen Cohn
Specialty: African goods
Exhibiting at: Santa Fe June 1995; 3rd International Bead Conference, Washington, D.C. November 1995; and Los Angeles Gift Show.

Payment: Cks-cash
Wholesale: $50 minimum
Mail Order: $50 minimum
Catalog: Free

Wholesale African goods. Beads, textiles, wood carvings, tools, etc.

CHESTER BEAD

205 Camino Alto #130
Mill Valley, CA 94941
Phone: 415-381-3934
Hours: Mon-Wed 12-5
   Thurs 12-7 Fri 12-5 Sat 11-4
Owner: Simma Chester
Specialty: Ethnic beads

Payment: Cks-Cash
Retail: Yes
Classes: Call for schedule
Restringing: Yes
Custom Work: Call for prices
Finished Pieces: Yes

A world traveler and committed bead devotee, Simma has the interest and enthusiam to help her customers with instruction, information, and a well-developed knowledge of the beads. In business since 1984, her selection is vast and extremely varied. New items are always coming in. A wide and eclectic selection of beads, unusual elements, unique findings, tools, books. If you want the exotic and offbeat, visit Chester Bead.

CHICO BEAD

804 Broadway
Chico, CA 95928
Phone: 916-345-8551
FAX: 916-872-5020
Hours: Mon-Sun 10-6
Owner: Shari Maxson Hopper
Specialty: Czech glass, seed beads to 20°
Exhibiting at: Northern California and Northwest Bead Society sales.

Payment: Cks-MC-Visa
Retail: Yes
Wholesale: $25 minimum
Mail Order: Limited - $25 min.
Classes: Call for schedule
Restringing: Call for prices
Finished Pieces: Yes

A large selection of beads and a helpful staff. Do it yourself work area with tools and assistance. Hot glass beadmaking is a specialty with guest teachers, five torches and related supplies and books. Finished jewelry for sale, consignment pieces and jewelry. Located in a small town, prices are low and the store is an old brick brewery building with an eclectic atmosphere. Every possible type of bead.

CREATIVE EXPRESSIONS OF PALM SPRINGS

1111 S. Palm Canyon Drive
Palm Springs, CA 92264
Phone: 619-327-2587
Hours: Mon-Sat 9-5
Owner: Priscilla P. Gonzales
Specialty: Quilting and beading

Payment: Cks-MC-Visa-AE
Retail: Yes
Mail Order: Yes
Classes: Call for schedule
Finished Pieces: Yes

All sizes of seed beads and all other kinds of beads and a complete quilt shop carrying bolts of 100% cotton fabric. Customers receive great service and every Thursday is beading workshop day.

CYNABAR DESIGNS

19323 Vanowen Street
Reseda, CA 91335
Phone: 818-609-7195
Fax: 818-783-0816
Hours: Mon-Sat 10-6 Sun 12-4
Owners: Barry and Cynthia Niedelman
Specialty: Gemstone beads

Payment: Cks-MC-Visa-AE
Retail: Yes
Wholesale: $100 minimum
Mail Order: Yes
Classes: Yes
Restringing: Yes
Finished Pieces: Yes

Small, personalized shop selling beads, findings, jewelry, rocks and fossils for collectors. Also gemstone beads and accents from around the world, wire wrapping, tools and bead cord.

DUE SOUTH IMPORTS

26715 Pariso Drive
Mission Viejo, CA 92691
Phone/Fax: 714-830-3156
Hours: Phone or FAX only
Owner: Bill Eames
Specialty: Guatemalan handicrafts

Payment: Cks-COD
Wholesale: $50 minimum
Mail Order: $50 minimum
Catalog: $2 price list
Finished Pieces: Yes

Importer of Guatemalan handicrafts including wedding chains, lattice beads, silver-coated beads (acid wash process), ceramic beads, ceramic suns, moons and others; silver charms, milagros of all shapes and silver washed belts and necklaces.

EAGLE BEADS

317 Mid-Valley Shopping Center
  6 miles from Carmel
Carmel Valley, CA 93923
Phone: 408-626-3575
Hours: Mon-Sat 10-5
Owner: Jack DeWitt
Specialty: White hearts, one-of-a-kind
Exhibiting at: Northern California Bead Society, Northwest Bead Society and Portland Bead Society bazaars.

Payment: Cks
Retail: Yes
Wholesale: $40 minimum
Mail Order: $40 minimum
Catalog: Free
Restringing: Call for cost
Custom Work: Call

You'll find the unique and unusual in this well-stocked and well-organized bead store. All kinds of beads with new arrivals weekly.

EL DORADO

213 Church Street at Market
San Francisco, CA 94114
Phone: 415-861-4515
Hours: Tues-Sun 11-7
  Mon. by appointment only
Owner: Harold Brennan
Specialty: Sterling silver

Payment: Cks-MC-Visa-AE
Retail: Yes
Wholesale: $100 minimum
Mail Order: Yes
Catalog: $2 refundable
Classes: By appointment
Restringing: Call for prices
Custom Work: Call for prices

A large selection of handmade lampwork, silver and antique beads. Antique charms, talismans, curios and custom jewelry design and repair available.

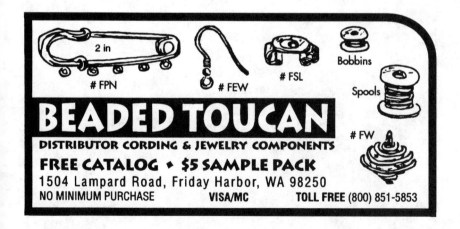

GLENN ERSO

Glenn has been designing unique and exquisite quality sterling silver beads and clasps since 1976. All of his components are entirely handcrafted in South Asia by silversmiths who have a long tradition of beadmaking. This is evident in the extremely high quality of their craftsmanship. Many of the beads and clasps are available in graduated sizes and shapes and most have a beautiful antique patina. All of the clasps and many of the beads can also be ordered in gold vermeil. The beads and clasps pictured on these two pages are only a small sampling of a very large selection.

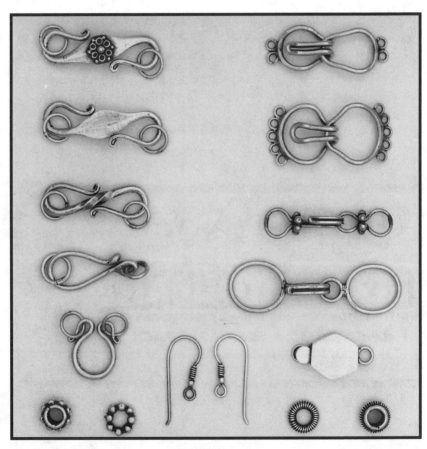

GLENN ERSO BEADS & CLASPS

7820 Broadway
Lemon Grove, CA 91945
Phone: 619-463-6644
Hours: Mon-Fri 9-5
Owner: Glenn Erso

Payment: Cks
Wholesale: $100 Minimum
Mail Order: Yes
Catalog: $2 refundable
$5 foreign. Mail requests only

Specialty: Silver and vermeil beads, clasps, earwires
Exhibiting at: Los Angeles Gift Show with Village Arts, Tucson Gem
and Mineral Show, February only at Holidome.

**GLENN ERSO -- Exquisite quality handwrought silver
and vermeil beads, clasps and components. Antique and
traditional South Asian reproductions.**

EXPEDITION

P. O. Box 4137
1708 'B ' M.L. King Jr. Way
Berkeley, CA 94704
Phone: 510-644-0110
FAX: 510-644-0166
Hours: Mon-Wed by appt. only
Owner: Dave Braun
Specialty: Carved jade, stone beads, sterling, ethnic beads
Exhibiting at: Northern California Bead Society Sale, May; Gem and Jewelry, San Mateo; San Francisco Gift Show, Northwest Bead Bazaar.

Payment: Cks-MC-Visa
Wholesale: $75 minimum
Mail Order: $75 minimum
Catalog: $2

Geared toward the professional bead stringer/designer. Offering the widest selection of fun design elements at truly competitive prices. Ethnic and contemporary and all the latest styles. Large collection of jade carvings and Czech glass beads. Display materials and tools.

FANTASY BEADS

946 W. College Avenue
Santa Rosa, CA 95401
Phone: 707-523-4356
Hours: Mon-Sat 10-6
Owner: Jeanne and Steve Seefeldt
Specialty: Handmade glass beads

Payment: Local Cks-MC-Visa
Retail: Yes
Wholesale: $40 minimum

Specializing in quality beads and findings. Always looking for new and exciting beads to add to the inventory. A large selection of handmade beads, sterling silver beads, findings and books. Also crystal, vintage glass, Fimo, ethnic, tools, bead boards andcharms.

FARRIN O'CONNOR DESIGN STUDIO & STORE

146 West Bellevue Drive
Pasadena, CA 91105
Phone: 818-796-1837
Hours: Tues-Sat 12-6
Owners: Margo Farrin
Specialty: Classes
Exhibiting at: The Society of Glass Beadmakers Gathering, August, 1995.

Payment: Cks
Retail: Yes
Classes: Call for schedule
Restringing: Call
Custom Work: Call
Finished Pieces: Yes

Studio store, gallery, books, supplies and much more. Lots of fine craft classes such as glass beadmaking and wire work. Beads from all over the world; antique, new, handmade, Czech glass, metal, raku and components; antique pendants, dangles and other artifacts that can be used in jewelry designs.

THE FASHION COMPANY

28 Carson Avenue
San Francisco, CA 94114
Phone: 415-626-5641
FAX: 415-861-1641
Hours: Call
Owner: Michael and Tasia Melvin
Specialty: Sourcing obscure items

Payment: Cks-MC-Visa
Wholesale: $75 minimum
Mail Order: $75 minimum
Catalog: Yes

A one-stop shop offering everything from A-Z, Austrian crystals to ziplock bags. Beads for Native American costumes, trims for the theatre, rhinestones for jewelry and much more. The sales staff is helpful and will place special orders.

FOGEL'S

1128 Wall Street
La Jolla, CA 92037
Phone: 619-456-2696
Hours: Tues-Sat 10-5
Owners: Dennis and Nina Fox
Specialty: Antique glass beads

Payment: Cks-MC-Visa-AE
Retail: Yes
Wholesale: Yes
Mail Order: Yes
Restringing: Call for quote
Custom Work: Call for quote
Finished Pieces: Yes

Fogel's carries an interesting variety of beads, components, stringing supplies, and findings. Specializing in antique beads and antique and estate jewelry. The shop is a charming delight nestled in the heart of The Village in beautiful La Jolla. Fogel's is a great store.

THE FOLK TREE COLLECTION

199 S. Fair Oaks Avenue
Pasadena, CA 91105
Phone: 818-793-4828
FAX: 818-793-4841
Hours: Mon-Wed 11-6
 Thurs-Fri 10-7 Sat 10-6 Sun 12-5
Owner: Rocky Behr
Specialty: Ethnic beads

Payment: Cks-MC-Visa-AE
Retail: Yes
Mail Order: Yes
Gallery: Call for information
Consignment: Call

Store and gallery located near historic Old Town Pasadena specializing in textiles, clothing, beads, jewelry, antiques, folk art and contemporary crafts from around the world. Beads from around the world of all materials including glass, stone, ceramic and wood.

Our specialty is antique beads.
European glass, precious, semi-precious, ethnic,
Austrian and Czechoslovakian crystal to name a few.
We also do stringing and carry an extensive
inventory of bead supplies to handle all your needs.

1128 Wall Street, La Jolla, CA 92037 (619) 456-2696

FRUGAL'S BEADS

3816 Bagley Avenue
Culver City, CA 90232
Phone/FAX: 310-837-3027
Hours: Tues-Sat 10:30-5
Owner: Paulette Storm
Specialty: Unique beads
Exhibiting at: Los Angeles Bead Society sales.

Payment: Cks-MC-Visa-AE
Retail: Yes
Wholesale: $50 minimum
Mail Order: Call
Classes: Call for schedule
Restringing: Yes
Finished Pieces: Yes

Unique beads and findings from all over the world including glass, seed and semiprecious. Full line of findings. tools, incredible inventory of one-of-a-kind finished pieces and vintage beads and designer costume jewelry. Personalized attention and instruction available. Always seeking new designers and innovative teachers.

FULL MOON BEADS

970 Second Street
Novato, CA 94947
Phone: 415-892-4677
FAX: 415-892-5117
Hours: Mon-Tues & Fri 10-6
 Wed-Thurs 10-7 Sat 10-5 Sun 11-4
Owners: Olivia and Larry Eckert
Specialty: Full Moon Club Card

Payment: Local Cks-MC-Visa
Retail: Yes
Wholesale: $100 minimum
Classes: Individual /Call
Restringing: Yes
Custom Work: Yes
Finished Pieces: Yes
Gallery: Call for details
Consignment: Yes

A unique store with a large selection of imported beads and beading supplies. Service oriented staff will assist you with ideas. Always an unusual mix of handmade and ethnic jewelry. 40% discount with tax number and no minimums; no tax number $100 minimum for 40% off. After 10 purchases the Club card gives you a store credit based on your average purchases.

GARDEN OF BEADIN'

P. O. Box 1535
Redway, CA 95560
752 Redwood Drive, Garberville
Phone: 707-923-9120
FAX: 707-923-9160
Orders: 1-800-BEAD LUV
Hours: Mon-Sat 9-6 Sun 11-5
Owner: Charlotte Silverstein
Specialty: Seed and antique beads

Payment: Cks-MC-Visa-AE
Retail: Yes
Wholesale: Yes
Mail Order: Yes
Catalog: $2
Classes: Call for schedule
Finished Pieces: Yes
Consignment: Yes

A helpful staff who will solve any technical problems you may have and answer any questions. All kinds of beads, new and antique, findings, books, handcrafted jewelry, gifts and antique purses.

GARGOYLE BEADS

1310 Haight Street @ Central
San Francisco, CA 94117
Phone: 415-552-4274
FAX: 415-861-8223
Hours: Mon-Sun 11-7
Owners: Jade Gunnarson
Specialty: Czech glass and ethnic

Payment: Cks-MC-Visa-AE
Retail: Yes
Wholesale: Yes
Mail Order: Yes
Classes: Call
Restringing: Yes
Custom Work: Yes
Finished Pieces: Yes

After designing jewelry professionally for eight years, Jade realized her passion of opening a bead store in the historic Haight Ashbury. An extensive selection, low prices and a comfortable atmosphere for jewelry makers to design their own creations in the store. Hepful, friendly staff and long hours, a bead store for beginners and professionals. **Mention The Bead Directory and receive 10% off all jewelry and loose beads.**

GEE JAY'S U NAME IT

211A West 19th @ C Street
Antioch, CA 94509
Phone: 510-757-4752
Hours: Wed-Thurs, Sat 10-6 Fri 11-8
Owners: Gary and Janice Coggiola
Specialty: Gold fill and sterling wire wrap

Payment: Cks
Retail: Yes
Wholesale: $50 minimum
Mail Order: On request
Classes: Call for list
Finished Pieces: Yes

Lots of beads and rock and mineral specimens, gifts from the earth, jewelry, wire wrap items, findings, books, rock polishing supplies and equipment. Helpful information, assistance and tips for bead or rockaholics to get you hooked on a new hobby guaranteed to reduce stress and get a look or two from admirers of your wearable art.

GENERAL BEAD

637 Minna Street
San Francisco, CA 94103
Phone: 415-621-8187
Hours: Tues-Sat 12-5
Owners: Michael and Steven Sunshine
Specialty: Japanese seed beads

Payment: Cks-MC-Visa
Retail: Yes
Wholesale: $100 minimum
Mail Order: $25 minimum
Catalog: $3

Over 18,000 items. Direct importers of Japanese seed beads with competitive prices. Also Czech and French seed beads, over 2,000 Swarovski pieces, excitingly different and exclusive beads from India made of Italian glass and Indian glass. Over 500 styles of brass charms, faux pearls and over 1,000 styles of antique sequins.

GLOBAL BEADS

720 Villa Street
Mt. View, CA 94041
Phone/FAX: 415-967-7556
Hours: Tues-Thurs 11-7 Fri 11-8
  Sat-Sun 11-6
Owners: Kathleen and Gary Susinetti
Specialty: Exotic beads

Payment: Cks-MC-Visa
Retail: Yes
Wholesale: Yes
Mail Order: $30 minimum
Restringing: Call for quote
Finished Pieces: Yes

Huge selection and great prices. Specializing in exotic beads and
unique focal pieces from Africa, Peru, Indonesia, India and Asia. A
vast selection of books, tools, buttons, findings, charms and castings.
A collection which excites, entices and stimulates the novice beader,
and the designer to create. Located in downtown Mt. View between
Castro and Hope Street.

GOTSIE'S TRADING CO.

P.O. Box 127
207 5th Street (downtown)
Huntington Beach, CA 92648
Phone/FAX: 714-969-7000
Hours: Mon-Sun /Call first
Owner: Marla and Leigh
Specialty: Quality and variety

Payment: Cks-MC-Visa
Retail: Yes
Wholesale: Yes
Classes: Call for schedule
Finished Pieces: Yes

A wide variety of beading supplies, along with knowledgeable and friendly advice. Japanese seed beads, delica, old Czech, glass, African and more. Also findings, sterling silver charms and earrings, tools and books.

GYPSY WIND BEAD & TRIM

147 Sacramento Street
Auburn, CA 95603
Phone: 916-823-1020
Hours: Mon-Sat 10:30-5
  Sun 11-5 Closed Tuesday
Owners: Bruce and Judee Webb
Specialty: Antique beads and buttons

Payment: Cks-MC-Visa
Retail: Yes
Wholesale: $30 minimum
Mail Order: $25 minimum
Catalog: $4
Restringing: Yes

Gypsy Wind is an importer and supplier of over 10,000 different beads including 1,200 seed and bugle beads on display. Hundreds of beads from the 1900 to 1960 era. Unusual old findings and over 3,000 styles of antique glass jewels. Favorite stop of antique dealers and designers. Truly a bead heaven for the jewelry designer.

HEART BEAD

761 8th Street, On the plaza
Arcata, CA 95521
Phone: 707-826-9577
FAX: 707-826-9583
Hours: Mon-Sat 11-6 Sun 12-5
Owners: Kim Wertz, Greg Galardy
Specialty: Creativity

Payment: Cks-MC-Visa-AE
Retail: Yes
Mail Order: Yes
Classes: Call for schedule
Restringing: Yes
Custom Work: Yes
Finished Pieces: Yes
Gallery: Yes

The friendly staff will show you how to design and help you assemble at no charge. A great selection of beads from all over the world from Kiffa to Fimo, chevrons to seed beads, Russian blue to Japanese Miracles and much more. Antique, vintage, new, findings, leather, books and tools.

HEART BEADS

20895 Redwood Road
Castro Valley, CA 94546
Phone: 510-881-5369
FAX: 510-881-5395
Hours: Tues-Wed-Fri 10:30-6
  Thurs 10:30-8   Sat 10:30-5
  Sun 12-5
Owners: Debbie Palmer and Lisa Allphin
Specialty: Great variety

Payment: Cks
Retail: Yes
Wholesale: $50 minimum
Classes: Call for schedule
Restringing: Yes
Custom Work: Yes
Finished Pieces: Yes

A fast growing, happy bead store. Always something new to discover and enthusiastic staff. Huge selection of all kinds of beads at very reasonable prices, free basic instruction. Classes in everything from peyote-stitch pouches to hand metalsmithing to kids classes. At Heart Beads, beading is a form of therapy. Easy to get to from Highway 580 and free, safe parking. Join them for one of their silly events (prizes, free classes, discounts and food). Books, tools, findings, cords, Fimo and beads from antique, ethnic to charms, Czech, ceramic and more.

MARKETING TIP: If you're going to start your own business and sell your beads and jewelry, you need to find the right market for your beadwork. Not every bead store, craft store or craft fair will be the right place to sell your work. Talk to other artists who do similar work and ask what worked best for them.

HIMALAYAN TRADING CO.

P. O. Box 99
Middletown, CA 95461
Phone: 707-987-2563 or 515-469-3629
Hours: Call
Owner: Quentin A. Wood
Specialty: Tibetan beads and ornaments
Exhibiting at: Whole Life Expos

Payment: Cks
Wholesale: $100 minimum
Mail Order: Yes
Catalog: Yes
Finished Pieces: Yes

Midwest office at 408 W. Lowe Avenue, Fairfield, IA 52556. Direct importer of beads and ornaments from Tibet and Nepal. Unique items no one else carries in the U.S. Brass, copper, silver, and many gemstone beads and ornaments. Also sacred symbols, prayer box lockets, Tibetan turquoise, lapis lazuli, carnelian, amber, fossilized Tibetan coral and Rudrakshan beads.

HOUSE OF BEADS

3229 Pico Boulevard
Santa Monica, CA 90405
Phone: 310-829-0349
Hours: Mon-Fri 11-5:30 Sat 11-5
Owners: Ron Porter, Jim Meshcon
Specialty: Quality glass beads

Payment: Local Cks-MC-Visa
Retail: Yes
Wholesale: $50 minimum
Discount: With resale no.
Restringing: Yes
Custom Work: Yes
Finished Pieces: Yes

Well organized store with an exceptional selection of quality merchandise. Everything needed to make necklaces, earrings, and bracelets and free advice in selection, design and fabrication. European glass, new and old, sterling silver, assorted metals, African trade beads, findings, stringing materials, tools and books. Knowledgeable service. Outstanding reputation and many referrals.

INTERNATIONAL BEAD & JEWELRY SUPPLY

5729 Erlanger Street
San Diego, CA 92122
Phone: 619-233-6822, 800-672-2211
FAX: 619-233-6827
Owner: Ralph Jaenicke
Hours: Mon-Sun 8-5
Specialty: Olive wood beads
    from Israel

Payment: Cks-MC-Visa
Wholesale: $50 minimum
Mail Order: $50 minimum
Catalog: $2
Restringing: Yes
Custom Work: Yes
Finished Pieces: Yes

Beads of glass, olive wood from Israel, colored wood from Taiwan and semiprecious chips, finished jewelry, findings and nativities and angels from Italy. Most shipments sent in 3 days via UPS.

JBJ ORIGINALS /JEWELS BY JUALS

P. O. Box 3560
Berkeley, CA 94703
Phone: 510-652-0780
Owner: Julie W. Gill
Hours: By appointment
Specialty: Limited editions
Custom Work: Yes

Payment: Cks
Retail: Yes
Wholesale: Yes
Mail Order: Yes
Classes: Group or private
Restringing: Yes
Finished Pieces: Yes

Distinctive, limited-edition necklaces and earrings featuring unique combinations of semiprecious stones, Swarovski crystals, antique and handblown glass, hand-painted Peruvian and ceramic beads. All necklaces hand-knotted on silk and finished with 14K gold-filled or sterling silver clasps. Custom orders welcome. Expert restringing.

KAHN-FAGAN

P. O. Box 3956
Santa Barbara, CA 93130-3956
Phone: 805-569-1574
Hours: Mon-Sat 9-6
Owner: Ellen Daniel Kahn-Fagan
Specialty: German and Czech
glass beads

Payment: Cks-M.O.
Retail: Yes
Wholesale: Yes
Mail Order: $50 minimum
Price/Product List: SASE
Finished Pieces: Yes
Custom Work: Yes
Restringing: Yes

Exhibiting at: Los Angeles Bead Society sales and the Santa Fe Bead Bazaar June '95. For other shows write to be added to mailing list.

European glass beads at reasonable prices, mostly vintage sold by the strand, gross and mixed beads by the 1/2 kilo. Stock changes constantly. Beads sold at shows, mail order or by appointment. African trade beads also available. Also manufacture one-of-a-kind fused glass pieces which are only available at shows. If you need a special bead or color it is best to send an example. Quantity discounts available at wholesale level. They also buy collections.

KATHERINE'S BEADS & SUPPLIES

22458 Barton Road
Grand Terrace, CA 92313
Phone: 909-825-5885
FAX: 909-875-3568
Hours: Mon-Fri 12-5 Sat 10-4
Owner: Katherine Pellegrine

Payment: Cks-MC-Visa
Retail: Yes
Wholesale: Yes
Classes: Call for schedule
Restringing: Yes
Custom Work: Yes
Finished Pieces: Yes

All kinds of beads including crystal, glass, shell, natural, Fimo, ethnic, and metal. Also supplies, findings, earring parts and classes.

LACIS

2982 Adeline Street
Berkeley, CA 94703
Phone: 510-843-7178
FAX: 510-843-5018
Hours: Mon-Fri 1-5:30 Sat 11-5
Owners: Jules and Kaethe Kliot

Payment: MC-Visa
Retail: Yes
Wholesale: Yes
Mail Order: Yes
Catalog: $4

A charming store that stocks tools, supplies and books for bead embroidery, lace making, costume and related textile arts. A small collection of antique beaded bags and beadwork from clothing.

LEGENDARY BEADS

483 South Main Street
Sebastopol, CA 95472
Phone: 707-829-7229
Hours: Daily 11-6
Owner: Jody McDonnell
Contact: Barbara Masklyne, Mgr.
Specialty: Contemporary glass beads

Payment: Cks-MC-Visa
Retail: Yes
Designer Discount: 20%
with resale number
on purchases over $50

Located in scenic Sonoma County, at Legendary Beads they love the beauty, myths and history of beads and pride themselves on bringing you an interesting and reasonably priced collection of exceptional beads and components.

LEGENDARY BEADS

112 Washington Street
Petaluma, CA 94952
Phone: 707-769-8385
Owner: Jody McDonnell
Hours: Tues-Sat 11-6 Sun 12-5
Specialty: Contemporary glass beads

Payment: Cks-MC-Visa
Retail: Yes
Designer Discount: 20% w/
resale number on
purchases over $50
Classes: Call for schedule

Travel through space and time on silken threads and rainbows of beads! Many different styles of bead art find expression through the selection of beads at Legendary Beads. Renowned artists share their own professional methods in their workshops, while other classes teach basic techniques and classic styles. A store and workspace with lots of really unique beads.

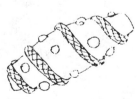

THE MAGICAL TRINKET

524 Hayes Street
San Francisco, CA 94102
Phone: 415-626-0764
Owner: Eve Blake
Hours: Tues-Sat 11-7 Sun 12-5
Specialty: Unique beads

Payment: Cks-MC-Visa
Retail: Yes
Wholesale: $25 minimum
Classes: Call for schedule
Restringing: Yes
Custom Work: Yes
Finished Pieces: Yes

A great bead store located in Hayes Valley between Octavia and Laguna offering ingredients to stimulate the crafty mind to create miniature works of wearable art. Books, magazines, antique and modern beads and findings. Staff will help you develop your own speical designs and help you put it together. Comfortable, easy going atmosphere in which to select the right beads. Also a gift store featuring the work of California artists working in beads, metal and glass. Special order work includes beaded clothing and accessories.

THE NAME GAME

505 So. Beverly Drive, Ste. 123
Beverly Hills, CA 90212
Phone: 310-284-3434
Fax: 310-552-8080
Hours: Mon-Fri 9-5
Owners: Alan and Gail Stewart
Specialty: Personalized wooden beads

Payment: Cks-MC-Visa
Retail: Yes
Wholesale: $300 minimum
Mail Order: Yes
Catalog: Free. Specify
   retail or wholesale

Manufacturers of wooden letter and symbol beads which are strung together to create necklaces and keychains.

NATIVE STAR CRAFTS

P. O. Box 115
Arcata, CA 95521
Phone: 707-839-8278, 800-290-8278
Hours: Call
Owner: Sylvia Soper
Specialty: Beadcraft kits

Payment: Cks
Retail: Yes
Wholesale: Min. 12 kits
Mail Order: Yes
Catalog: Free brochure
Finished Pieces: Yes
Custom Work: Yes

Home studio with beadwork and beadcraft kits. Beginner's beaded earring kits in triangle (Comanche) or tube (peyote) style. Each available in five colors. Children's beadcraft kits make at least three bracelets or necklaces in three colors. Suggested ages 8+. Kits wholesale @ $3.50 each. Minimum one dozen, quantity discounts available.

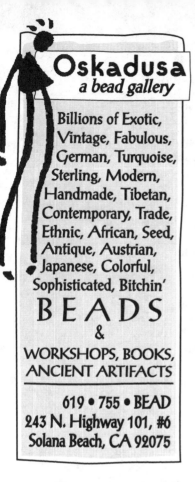

RITA OKRENT
439 Veteran Avenue
Los Angeles, CA   90024
Phone: 310-472-1895
Hours: By appointment only
Specialty: Unique ethnic designs

Payment: Inquire
Wholesale: $50 minimum
Mail Order: Yes
Finished Pieces: Yes

Exhibiting at: Los Angeles Bead Society sales and 3rd International Bead Conference, Washington D.C., November 1995.

Jewelry designer and bead seller since 1973. Rita and her husband travel around the world and bring back beads from many foreign countries such as Egypt, Morocco, China and Hong Kong. Beads include ancient glass beads from Syria, antique beads from England and also textiles from Africa.

51 California

ORB WEAVER

4793 Telegraph Avenue
Oakland, CA 94609
Phone: 510-658-0452, 510-658-8131
Hours: Mon-Fri 11-7
  Sat 11-6 Sun 12-5
Owner: Jean Astrinsky
Specialty: The uncommon
Custom Work: Yes

Payment: Cks-MC-Visa
Retail: Yes
Discount: 20% w/resale
Mail Order: Yes
Catalog: $2
Classes: Call for schedule
Restringing: Yes
Finished Pieces: Yes
Gallery Space: Yes

Established in 1980, offering the most exciting and diverse selection of beads and embellishments in California including a large selection of metal stampings and castings. Friendly, helpful staff will answer your questions and assist you in design. A wide variety of unique classes available. A MUST SEE STORE!

OSKADUSA: A BEAD GALLERY

243 N. Highway 101 #6
At The Boardwalk
Solana Beach, CA 92075
Phone: 619-755-2323
Hours: Mon-Fri 10-6
  Sat 10-5 Sun 11-4
Owners: Lauren and Tina McChrie
Specialty: Antique and vintage beads

Payment: Cks-MC-Visa
Retail: Yes
Designer Discount: Yes
Classes: Call for schedule
Restringing: Yes
Custom Work: Yes
Gallery Space: Yes

Called a bead gallery because they concentrate on unusual, hard to find beads and components. They handpick each piece and are known for always having unique beads and artifacts. Other specialties are buttons and trims, one-of-a-kind collector pieces, metallic cords, French ribbons, books on beading, embroidery and fiber arts. Great workshops with knowledgeable instructors sharing innovative techniques. Come shop in an atmosphere of creativity and fun.

OUT ON A WHIM

121 E. Cotati Avenue
Cotati, CA 94931
Phone: 707-664-8343
FAX: 707-664-8353
Hours: Tues-Sat 11-6 Extended during Christmas season
Owners: Shawn and Beki Haley

Payment: Cks-MC-Visa-AE
Retail: Yes
Wholesale: $25 minimum
Mail Order: Yes
Catalog: Free

Specialty: Quality and service

A vast array of beads from every corner of the world. Over 5,000 styles of beads, 500 colors of seed beads. Every size, shape and color can be found in this store run by owners who are committed to quality, selection and service, all at competitive prices. Retail, wholesale and distributor prices available.

PALO PACIFICA BEADS

213 Grand Avenue
Pacific Grove, CA 93950
Phone/FAX: 408-647-9323
Hours: Mon-Sat 10-6
Owners: Kathy and Shannon Scott
Specialty: Design assistance

Payment: Cks-MC-Visa
Retail: Yes
Wholesale: $25 minimum
Classes: Call for schedule
Restringing: Yes
Custom Work: Yes
Finished Pieces: Yes
Gallery: Yes

Exhibiting at: Northern California Bead Society sales and The Whole Bead Show, Monterey, California.

Mother and daughter owned business dedicated to bringing you the very best in bead selection, quality and service. Direct importers offering affordable prices and a wide selection of beads from India, Malaysia, China and Poland. An extensive collection of ancient, authentic, ethnic and contemporary beads. Instructions and ideas offered to assist you in creating your own unique pieces. Special orders available and their own jewelry line. Five minutes from Carmel and Monterey, a truly unique sanctuary for bead lovers.

PENINSULA BEAD & SUPPLY

5166A Moorpark Avenue
San Jose, CA 95129
Phone: 408-253-6434
FAX: 408-253-6652
Hours: Mon-Fri 11-7
  Sat 11-6 Sun 12-5
Owner: Nancy Donnelly

Payment: Cks-MC-Visa-AE
Retail: Yes
Wholesale: $30 minimum
Mail Order: $15 minimum
Catalog: $5
Classes: Call for schedule
Restringing: Yes
Finished Pieces: Yes

All kinds of beads and beading supplies with the best prices. Friendly staff will assist anyone wanting to learn the basic beading for free. Stop by and compare.

PERL HOUSE

2311 Glendale Galleria
Glendale, CA 91210
Phone: 818-547-0537
Hours: Mon-Fri 10-9
 Sat 10-7 Sun 11-6
Owner: Laura Walker

Payment: Local Cks-MC
 Visa-Discover
Retail: Yes
Wholesale: Yes
Restringing: Yes
Custom Work: Yes
Finished Pieces: Yes

Customers may create their own costume jewelry while in the store. All kinds of beads (except seed and bugle) and tools.

THE PERUVIAN BEAD COMPANY

493 E. Main Street
Ventura, CA 93001
Phone: 805-641-1326
FAX: 805-642-0986
Hours: Mon-Sat 10:30-5
Owners: Steve and Juana Jelen
Specialty: Ethnic beads
Exhibiting at: Santa Fe and Los Angeles Bead Society sales

Payment: Cks-MC-Visa-AE
Retail: Yes
Wholesale: $100 minimum
Catalog: $2
Finished Pieces: Yes

Opened in 1988 and growing every year. Workspace, advice and assistance with ideas and project. Beautiful beads from all over the world. Also a range of ethnic and exotic jewelry from extensive travelling in the third world every year. All kinds of beads and findings, some manufactured especially for them. Also seed beads, glass beads and a huge selection of silver beads.

THE PLACE TO BEAD

2435 San Ramon Valley Boulevard
San Ramon, CA 94583
Phone: 510-866-2828
Hours: Call. Hours are seasonal
 Open 7 days
Owner: Julie Froines
Specialty: Customer service and trunk shows

Payment: Cks-MC-Visa
Retail: Yes
Wholesale: $30 minimum
Catalog: Available soon
Classes: Call for expanded
 1995 schedule
Finished Pieces: Yes

Recently expanded with even more beads this store ppecializes in friendly service for the beginner and the professional designer. At least six trunk shows a year with great prices and amazing selection with demonstrations by well known importers and artists such as Liza Wataghani, Donna Milliron, Bohemia Glass and Crystal Vintage Glass. A vast assortment of beads and findings of all types including new, antique, Indian glass, seed beads, Japanese Miracle beads, Austrian crystal, semiprecious stones and rare and unusual centerpieces. The knowledgeable staff will assist you with design and assembly.

REEDTZ BEADS

238 E Street
Davis, CA 95616
Phone: 916-758-0670
Hours: Mon-Sat 10-6 Sun 12-4
Owner: Carrie Sparrevohn
Specialty: Great customer service

Payment: Cks-MC-Visa
Retail: Yes
Wholesale: Yes

A family-run business, Reedtz Beads (in Davis, just fifteen minutes from downtown Sacramento) originally took pride in having one of the largest seed bead inventories in the Valley but now have dramatic and diverse larger beads as well.

RITUAL ADORNMENTS

2708 Main Street
Santa Monica, CA 90405
Phone: 310-452-4044
Hours: Tues-Sun 11-6
Owner: Cynthia Cummins and
Joel Mikkalson
Specialty: Sterling silver beads

Payment: Cks-MC-Visa
Retail: Yes
Designer Discount: Yes
Mail Order: Yes
Restringing: Call for quote
Custom Work: Yes
Finished Pieces: Yes

Located on historic Main Street in Santa Monica they stock a huge selection of quality beads at excellent prices. The owners hand pick all of the stock and specialize in Venetian glass, vintage, crystal, semiprecious stone and rare old collectable beads. The staff offers free consultation and custom design with purchase of beads. If you like to search for unusual treasure, this store is a must. **See the color insert for a photo of a selection of their beads.**

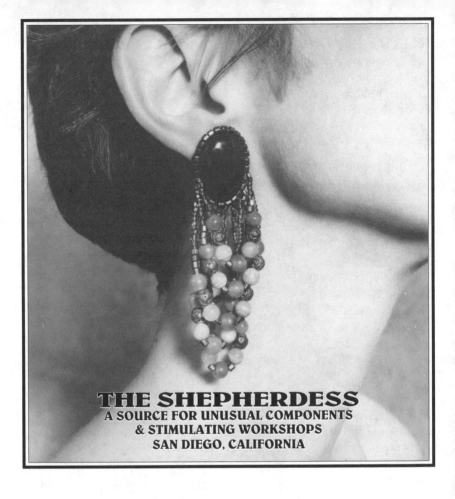

THE SHEPHERDESS
A SOURCE FOR UNUSUAL COMPONENTS
& STIMULATING WORKSHOPS
SAN DIEGO, CALIFORNIA

THE SHEPHERDESS
2802 Juan Street #14
San Diego, CA 92110
Phone: 619-297-4110
FAX: 619-297-9897
Hours: Mon-Sat 10-6   Sun 11-5
Owners: William Dubin, Marcie Stone
Specialty: Great bead workshops

Payment: Cks-MC-Visa-AE
Retail: Yes
Mail Order: Yes
Catalog: $2
Classes: Yes, free catalog
Custom Work: Yes
Finished Pieces: Yes
Consignment: Yes

Over 120 classes in beadwork, wearable art and embellishment-related subjects. New--1,200 sq. ft. of additional class space. Their teachers are the finest local artists and most renowned guest artists in the country. They also sell every type of bead and tool you'll need to make your own jewelry and finished jewelry and ethnic treasures.

SPOTTED PONY

P. O. Box 6245
San Pablo, CA 94806-6245
Phone: 510-758-4335
Hours: By appointment
Owner: Lori S. Berry
Book Price: $10.95 & $3 postage

Payment: Call
Retail: Yes
Wholesale: $60 minimum
Mail Order: Yes
Catalog: $1
Classes: Call for information
Finished Pieces: Yes

Designer of beaded jewelry and author of the book *How To Bead Earrings: An Artistic Approach* . Lori's beadwork is shown in *The New Beadwork*. She is an instructor of beading techniques and specializes in creation of one-of-a-kind beaded earrings, pendants, buckles and neck pieces.

STRING BEAD

163 E. 3rd Street
Chico, CA 95928
Phone: 916-894-2323
Hours: Mon-Sat 10-6 Sun 12-5
Owners: Kari and Robert Madera

Payment: Cks-MC-Visa
Retail: Yes
Mail Order: Yes
Classes: Call for schedule
Finished Pieces: Yes
Restringing: Call for quote

Create your own jewelry right on the spot. The friendly and helpful staff will assist in create your own unique jewelry at no extra charge. Choose from the selection of thousands of different beads from around the world. Everyone feels right at home at String Bead. Also how-to books, lots of findings and wire and tools.

'SWEETS'

7763-1/2 Beverly Boulevard
Los Angeles, CA 90036
Phone: 213-933-7922
Hours: Tues-Sat 9:30-5
Owner: Susan Elias

Payment: Cks-MC-Visa
Retail: Yes
Wholesale: Yes
Restringing: Yes
Custom Work: Yes
Finished Pieces: Yes

'Sweets' bead store is small in size but giant in variety and helpful service. All types of beads from all countries. Also tools, books, findings and novelties.

U BEAD IT

2525 Yorktown Avenue
Sacramento, CA 95821
Phone: 916-488-2323
Hours: Mon-Fri 10-6 Sat 10-5 Sun 12-4

Payment: Cks-MC-Visa
Retail: Yes
Wholesale: Yes
Mail Order: $25 minimum

Beads from around the world including Japanese, delicas, old and new glass, semiprecious, crystal, sterling silver and books and classes.

WILD THING'S

849 E. Stanley Boulevard
Livermore, CA 94550
Phone: 510-447-9453
Hours: Mon-Thurs 10-6
Fri-Sat 10-7 Sun 12-4
Owners: J-me and Vi
Specialty: Unusual beads and great service

Payment: Cks-MC-Visa
Retail: Yes
Wholesale: Yes
Mail Order: Yes
Classes: Call for schedule
Custom Work: Yes
Finished Pieces: Yes

Family run business with a friendly atmosphere where you can come and create your own jewelry in the store. Beads from all over the world, stained glass, jewelry, artwork, rocks, crystals, and several beadmakers exclusive to their store. Bead parties available with special days for kids, seniors and veterans. **Discount Coupon in the back of the Directory.**

YONE

478 Union Street
San Francisco, CA 94133
Phone: 415-986-1424
Hours: Thurs-Sat 12-4, others hours by appointment
Owners: Hermon Baker
Specialty: Great selection

Payment: Cks-MC-Visa
Retail: Yes
Wholesale: $25 minimum
Mail Order: $10 minimum

This store has been a "beehive of beads" since the 60's. Specializing in the widest possible selection of unusual and usual beads. Originally founded as a cooperative of artists and clothing designers interested in Asian art, the shop has branched out and now offers a selection of beads in every size, shape, material and color from all over the world. Yone caters to professional and amateur designers and artists. Prices are reasonable. A must see while in San Francisco.

Light years beyond the basics...

AMALLAMA

P. O. Box 774751
Downtown 7th & Lincoln
Steamboat Springs, CO 80477
Phone: 303-879-9127
FAX: 303-879-8071
Hours: During Season Mon-Sun 10-9
Owners: Tara and Larry Stroman

Payment: Cks-MC-Visa-AE
Retail: Yes
Restringing: Yes
Custom Work: Yes
Finished Pieces: Yes

While visiting the scenic valley town of Steamboat Springs be sure to make a "bead-line" to Amallama. Beads from all over the world – Africa, Japan, Peru and more! The friendly staff speaks "bead" and they're ready to assist anyone from beginners to designers in finding just the right components. Large selection of unusual loose beads, plus beads by the strand. Authentic folk art, exotic imported jewelry, leather and other natural fiber outerwear, and rugs, belts and hats.

BEADS AND BEYOND

Box 2935, Durango CO 81302
103 East 7th Avenue
Durango, CO 81301
Phone: 303-247-1204
Hours: Mon-Sat 10-6 Sun 12-5
  Longer hours in summer
Owners: Nancy Juliana and
  Ashley Dove
Specialty: Large selection

Payment: Local Cks-MC-Visa
Retail: Yes
Mail Order: Yes
Classes: Sept through May
Custom Work: Yes
Finished Pieces: Yes
Consignment: Yes

A wide selection of beads and jewelry making supplies. Cater to everyone from the professional to the beginner. Knowledgable friendly, staff will help you create your own beaded masterpieces. All sizes seed beads, semiprecious, contemporary glass, metal, Czech, African trade beads and much more. African art, leather and leather tools, findings, books, bead kits, wooden looms, and art to wear.

INTERNATIONAL BEADTRADER INC.

3435 S. Broadway, Corporate Ofc.
Englewood, CO 80110
Phone: 303-781-2657 800-805-2323
FAX: 303-781-5390
Hours: Mon-Fri 8:30-5
Owner: Jim Brock
Specialty: All kinds

Payment: Cks-MC-Visa
Retail: Yes
Wholesale: $50 minimum
Mail Order: $20 retail
Catalog: $5 refundable
Classes: Call stores for schedule

Direct importer of a wide variety of beads from all over the world.
Both the retail stores and wholesale/mail order warehouse offer a vast
selection of beads, findings, and supplies in quantities to accommodate
the beader, jewelry designer, or retailer. Fourteen retail stores in
Wisconsin, Oklahoma, Kansas, Colorado, Nebraska, Missouri and
Illinois . All kinds of seed beads, ethnic, metals, charms and books.

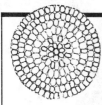
MORNING FLOWER PRESS

P. O. Box 11443
Denver, CO   80211
Phone: 303-477-8442
FAX: Same, call first
Hours: By appointment
Owner: Z. Susanne Aikman
Specialty: Native American

Payment: Cks
Retail: Yes
Wholesale: Yes
Mail Order: Yes
Catalog: SASE
Classes: Call for information
Custom Work: Yes
Finished Pieces: Yes

Exhibiting at: Local Powwows and cultural events.

Self publishing Native American Indian beadwork publications and
instructional videos since 1979. Museum-quality finished beadwork,
restoration, repair and personal ornaments. Instructor available to
institutions and groups.

MORNING LIGHT EMPORIUM

P. O. Box 1155
1326 Highway 133
Paonia, CO 81428
Phone: 303-527-4493
FAX: Call first
Hours: 11-5 Clsd Wed and Sun,
Owner: Roxy Grinnell
Specialty: Seed beads
Exhibiting at: Tyson Wells, Quartzsite, Arizona.

Payment: Cks-MC-Visa
Retail: Yes
Wholesale: Bulk only
Mail Order: Yes
Catalog: Free
Restringing: Yes
Custom Work: Yes
Finished Pieces: Yes

For a bead store located almost in the middle of nowhere, they offer an amazing selection of beads from around the world including over 200 colors of size 11° seed beads, a large variety of glass, stone and metal beads, stringing supplies and looms. Other sales outlet: A Haggle of Vendors Emporium, 510 Main St., Grand Junction, CO. Open 10-5:30.

ONE OF A KIND

309 8th Street
Glenwood Springs, CO 81601
Phone: 303-945-5222
Hours: Mon-Sat 10-5:30
Owners: Pat Patterson and
   Murray Reynolds
Specialty: Rare and unusual beads

Payment: Cks-MC-Visa
Retail: Yes
Mail Order: Yes
Restringing: Yes
Finished Pieces: Yes
Gallery: Yes

Emphasis on culturally important beads from world sources. All kinds of beads from Asia, Africa and Europe. Owners have collected and sold beads for 25 years. Many of their beads are available nowhere else. Knowledgeable and helpful and glad to discuss beads anytime. Also selling their own handmade gold and silver jewelry, fine native art and crafts, textiles, ceramics and folk art.

ORNAMENTAL RESOURCES

Box 3010-BD
1427 Miner Street (by appt. only)
Idaho Springs, CO 80452
Phone: 303-567-2222, 800-876-6762
FAX: 303-567-4245
Hours: Mon-Fri 9-5
Specialty: Rare and unusual

Payment: Cks-MC-Visa-AE
Retail: Yes
Wholesale: $50 min. 1st order
Mail Order: Yes
Catalog: $25
Owners: Mary Broyles, Stan
   Broyles, George Sumpter

Primarily mail order offering rare and unusual beads and ornaments plus all the basic supplies needed for jewelry making. An exceptionally broad range of decorative materials for designers, artists, sculptors and craftspeople in jewelry and accessories, as well as clothing and costume embellishments. Continually refreshing this palette with new offerings.

PEARLS & JEWELS BEAD SHOP

1457 S. Pearl Street
Denver, CO 80210
Phone: 303-744-6944
Hours: Tues-Fri 12-6 Sat- Sun 12-5
Owners: Renna Shesso and
Hannah Reese
Specialty: Expert help and bead searches

Payment: Cks-MC-Visa-AE
Retail: Yes
Wholesale: $100 minimum
Classes: Call for schedule
Restringing: $15/hour
Finished Pieces: Yes

Awarded Denver's "Best Bead Shop - 1993" by Westword newspaper. Selling the most beautiful, sought-after, useful and eclectic selection of beads and findings. Both owners have done beadwork since childhood and have over seventy years of combined beading experience to offer customers expert assistance and excellent classes in all beadworking traditions. A charming and comfortable store where beading hearts can meet. Beads from around the world and unique beads and pendants by area artists.

PROMENADE'S LE BEAD SHOP

1970 13th Street
Boulder, CO 80302
Phone: 303-440-4807
Hours: Call for summer
and winter hours
Owner: Therese Spears
Specialty: Czech glass

Payment: Cks-MC-Visa-AE
Retail: Yes
Wholesale: Yes
Mail Order: Yes
Catalog: $2.50
Classes: Call for schedule
Restringing: Yes

Specializing in seed beads sizes 8°-12°. A "one stop bead shop" for stringing materials, fantasy beads, semiprecious and findings.

SILVER & BEADS

240 Pine Street
Ft. Collins, CO 80524
Phone: 303-221-9323
FAX: 303-484-3684
Hours: Mon-Sat 12-5
Owner: Suyi Liu
Specialty: Silver supplies and Asian antiques

Payment: Cks-MC-Visa-AE
Retail: Yes
Wholesale: $300 minimum
Mail Order: $100 minimum
Restringing: Yes
Custom Work: Yes
Finished Pieces: Yes

Semiprecious stone, sterling silver, antique glass and one-of-a-kind contemporary glass beads, finished jewelry, Asian and African antiques and fabrics. Personal service, will assist customers to design their own jewelry from their vast variety of beads and educate people who are interested in collecting by sharing with them the history and origin of beads. Suyi also designs jewelry with sterling silver wire and beads.

SKYLOOM FIBRES dba MILLIE FIORES

1705 S. Pearl
Denver, CO 80210
Phone: 303-777-2331
Hours: Mon-Sat 10-6
  Thurs 10-8 Sun 12-5
Owner: Charlotte Elich
Specialty: Unique and unusual beads

Payment: Cks-MC-Visa
Retail: Yes
Wholesale: Indian beads only
Classes: Call for schedule

Inside Skyloom Fibres, a sprawling yarn and fiber store, is Millie Fiores, a store within a store catering to the beader searching for the unusual. Stocking thousands of beads, collector's items from Africa, antique Czech and German glass, one-of-a-kind handworked glass pieces and metal and glass from India. Charms of all shapes and sizes, Indonesian silver and semiprecious stones, and everything needed to create your own pieces. Findings, beading cords, tool and books.

WORLDBEADS

2640 East 3rd Avenue
Denver, CO 80206
Phone: 303-388-3743
Hours: Mon-Sat 10-6 Sun 12-5
Owner: BeadWorks
Specialty: Unique selection

Payment: Cks-MC-Visa-AE
Retail: Yes
Wholesale: Yes
Mail Order: Yes
Restringing: Call for quote
Custom Work: Call for quote
Finished Pieces: Yes

Make your own jewelry store. Come in and create your own unique jewelry from the selection of beads and findings from around the world.

CONNECTICUT

BEADAZZLED

321 W. Putnam Avenue
Greenwich, CT 06830
Phone: 203-629-1516
FAX: 203-629-1566
Hours: Mon-Fri 9-5
Owner: Eric Russack

Payment: Cks-MC-Visa
Wholesale: Only
Mail Order: Yes
Catalog: $5

A wholesale bead company that prides itself on giving customers a quality fashion forward product. They carry over 10,000 different styles of beads and specialize in creative finishes and dyes of endless colors which they create on the premise and are made to order.

BEADWORKS®

The Finest Shops

• Greenwich, (203) 629-4500 • South Norwalk, (203) 852-9194
• Baltimore, (410) 732-2323 • Towson, (410) 583-2570 • Boston, (617) 247-7227
• Cambridge, (617) 868-9777 • Philadelphia, (215) 413-2323
• Newport, (401) 846-1440 • Providence, (401) 861-4540
• Fort Worth, (817) 625-2323 • Plano, (214) 881-2117

The Best Catalog

Thousands of superb beads illustrated in full color, full size reproduction. Our contemporary range is chosen by experienced buyers and designers in the United States and Europe.

A visual pleasure for bead lovers and a helpful reference for designers. Enjoy our rich collection of beads from Asia, Europe, Africa and the Americas.

For your copy, please send $10.00 to:
Beadworks Catalog
Riverside Plaza, 149 Water Street, Norwalk, CT 06854
Or Call (203) 852-9108 for Credit Card Orders

Beadworks® is a registered U.S. trademark of Beadworks International, Inc.

BEADWORKS
139 Washington Street
South Norwalk, CT 06854
Phone: 203-852-9194 or 9108
FAX: 203-855-8015
Hours: Mon-Fri 10:30-5:30
Sat 10-6 Sun 12-5
Owner: Nancy Wall
Specialty: Unique beads

Payment: Cks-MC-Visa
Retail: Yes
Wholesale: $300 minimum
Mail Order: Yes
Catalog: $10
Classes: Call for schedule
Restringing: $20/hour

The original Beadworks store, home base of jewelry designer and co-founder of Beadwork group, Nancy Wall. The catalog is in full color and features unique beads from all over the world. Also a full line of books, tools and findings and always new beads and new ideas.

65 Connecticut

Watch Us, Inc.

500B Monroe Tpke/Suite 351, Monroe, CT 06468
Telephone: (203) 736-0127 Fax: (203) 735-2891

★ LARGEST SELECTION OF CONTEMPORARY AND SOUTHWESTERN WATCH HEADS AND WATCH FINDINGS ★

WATCH US, INC.
500B Monroe Turnpike, Suite 351
Monroe, Connecticut 06468
Phone: 203-736-0127
FAX: 203-735-2891
Hours: Mon-Fri 9-5
Owner: Nancy

Payment: COD-MC-Visa-AE
Wholesale: $100 minimum
Catalog: $5 Refundable
Mail Order: Yes
Custom Work: Yes
Finished Pieces: Yes

Watch Us has the largest selection of watch heads, sterling silver cast findings and gold and silver metal attachments in the U.S. You will never think of beading a watch to the pin again! Custom design work available. Always something new! A bead your own watch book is available. Call for details.

DELAWARE

MAD CAT

4737 Concord Pike
Wilmington, DE 19803
Phone: 302-477-0579
FAX: 610-975-0299
Hours: Mon-Sat 10-9:30 Sun 12-5
Owner: Jacqueline Meaker
Specialty: Unique pieces

Payment: Cks-MC-Visa-AE
Retail: Yes
Wholesale: Yes
Mail Order: Yes
Classes: Call for schedule
Restringing: Call for prices
Finished Pieces: Yes

Jacqueline travels the world buying beads, ethnic jewelry, textiles, cultural arts and offers many unique one-of-a-kind pieces. Handblown glass, stone, ceramic, handpainted, lapis and semiprecious beads.

DISTRICT OF COLUMBIA

BEADAZZLED

1522 Connecticut Avenue N.W.
Washington, D.C. 20036
Phone: 202-265-2323
FAX: 301-608-0518
Hours: Mon,Tues, Sat, Sun 11-6
  Wed-Fri 10-7:30
Owners: Penny and
  Erik Diamanti de Widt
Specialty: Quality beads

Payment: Cks-MC-Visa-AE
Retail: Yes
Mail Order: Yes
Catalog: $5
Classes: Call for schedule
Restringing: Call for price
Custom Work: Call for quote
Finished Pieces: Yes
Consignment: Yes
Gallery: Yes

Exhibiting at: Baltimore, Washington D.C. and Virginia Bead Society sales, dates vary, call for information.

Beads of every sort from everywhere with beads for collectors and beginners in this clean, well-lit, inspiring environment. Antique, contemporary, ethnic, gemstones, glass, sterling, 14K, gold filled, brass, copper, amber, coral, clay, porcelain and plastic. Seed beads, fetishes, amazing selection of strands: trade beads, Czech and Indian glass. Knowledgeable and helpful staff and free how-to handouts. Tools, wide selection of findings, stringing materials and a great selection of bead books. Their goal is to help unleash your creativity through beads and direct importing keeps the prices down.

HARMATTAN ARTS OF AFRICA

1701 Bay Street, S.E. (Capitol Hill)
Washington, D.C. 20003
Phone: 202-544-8444
Hours: By appointment
Owner: Cheryl Olkes
Specialty: African beads and old Venetian

Payment: Cks-MC-Visa-AE
Retail: Yes
Mail Order: Yes
Finished Pieces: Yes

A gallery of traditional African art of interest to collectors with a large inventory of sculpture and textiles and a significant array of beads that have been used in Africa, Venetian, millefiore, Czech and made in Africa metal and sandcast, sold by the string or in finished necklaces. Not a catalog operation, this one-person business serves individual clients in person, on the telephone and through direct correspondence.

FLORIDA

THE BEAD GYPSIES INC.

P. O. Box 470
St. Petersburg, FL 33731-0470
Phone: 813-825-0069
Hours: By appointment only
Owners: Elinor Gollay and Rex Brasell
Specialty: Unusual beads
Exhibiting at: Call for 1995 schedule

Payment: Cks-MC-Visa-AE
Retail: Yes
Wholesale: $250 minimum
Mail Order: $25 minimum
Catalog: Call for price

Wholesale showroom and selling at retail shows in the Southeastern United States. A pendant catalog is being developed. They sell new, old, unusual, hard to find beads of every description from all over the world and pendants, charms and milagros.

THE BEAD STRING

1336 Cesery Boulevard
Jacksonville, FL 32211
Phone: 904-744-0746
Hours: Tues-Fri 10-6 Sat 10-4:30
Owner: Vivian L. Heath
Specialty: Great beads

Payment: Cks-MC-Visa
Retail: Yes
Designer Discount: Yes
Mail Order: Yes
Classes: Call for schedule
Restringing: Yes
Custom Work: Yes

Gemstone, seed, cloisoine, porcelain, wood, crystal, glass and many other ethnic beads. Also buttons in natural materials, custom design, jewelry for weddings or just for a new outfit or they will show you how to make your own. Free classes in basic bead stringing, and much more. You only pay for materials used. How-to books, stringing materials, findings and tumbled gemstones.

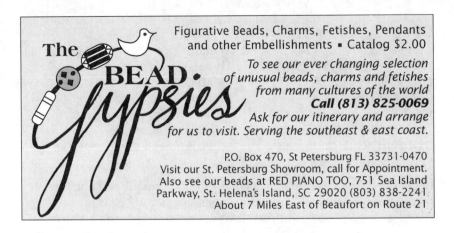

BEADS F.O.B.

6690 Superior
Sarasota, FL 34231
Phone: 813-921-0871
FAX: 813-349-2052
Hours: Mon-Fri 10-5 Sat 10-4
Owner: Marty Montague

Payment: Cks-MC-Visa
Retail: Yes
Classes: Call for schedule
Restringing: Yes
Finished Pieces: Yes
Gallery: Yes

A retail bead establishment specializing in "beads of value" natural stone, imported glass, crystal, amber, sterling and gold-filled, etc. Charms, select pendants, sculpture, and other related items. Also a complete selection of findings, tools, and books. Marty teaches classes in beading and handles repairs.

CHEVRON TRADING POST & BEAD COMPANY, INC.

2320 N. Monroe Street
Tallahassee, FL 32303
Phone: 904-385-3500 or 881-2323
FAX: 904-531-0139
Hours: Mon-Sat 10-7 Sun 12-5
Owner: Deborah Coule
Specialty: Old world trade beads
Exhibiting at: AIA Indian Festival,
   Fairgrounds, Orlando, November

Payment: Cks-MC-Visa-Discover
Retail: Yes
Wholesale: $50 minimum
Mail Order: $25 minimum
Catalog: Free color
Classes: Call for schedule
Restringing: Call for quote
Custom Work: Call for quote

Largest bead shop in the southeast. Wholesale and retail sales, modern glass beads, findings, pendants, large selection of old world trade beads, specializing in the chevron bead and millefiores. Finished jewelry, necklaces, beaded watches, award winning pieces by Deborah Coule. Very service oriented. Seed beads in 100's of colors.

69 Florida

CRYSTAL CREATIONS

4535 Summit Boulevard
West Palm Beach, FL 33415
Phone: 407-686-1139
FAX: 407-688-1746
Hours: Tues, Wed, Fri-Sat 10-6
  Thurs 10-8 Sat 10-6
Owners: Glenda Paunonen
Specialty: Semiprecious beads

Payment: Cks-MC-Visa
Retail: Yes
Wholesale: Yes
Mail Order: Yes
Classes: Call for schedule
Restringing: Call for quote
Finished Pieces: Yes
Consignment: Call for details

Large selection of beads featuring hard-to-find, unique and one-of-a-kind pieces. Specializing in semiprecious stones and beads of all shapes and sizes, along with crystals and gemstone jewelry. Also a wide range of seed, cloisone, glass, wood, ethnic, trade, crystal, antique and collector beads. Large assortment of sterling silver, brass, copper and bronze pendants. Books, tools and findings (including sterling silver and gold filled). Their own line of custom designed jewelry and a staff of cheerful creative designers to help with your selections. Special Beader's Club for frequent shoppers.

D. J. WHIMSY! BEADS UNLIMITED

6534 Gateway Avenue
Sarasota, FL 34231
Phone: 813-925-9989,
  800-357-8085
Hours: Mon, Wed, Fri 11-6
  Tues, Thurs 11-7 Sat 11-5
Owner: Deni and Jeff Dreazen
Specialty: Love of beads

Payment: Cks-MC-Visa-Discover
Retail: Yes
Wholesale: $50 minimum
Mail Order: $15 minimum
Catalog: Video $3
Classes: Call for schedule
Restringing: Call for quote
Custom Work: Call for quote

A multi-faceted bead shop offering classes for all levels, children's classes, bead parties, gift classes, crystal workshops and artisan days. The staff is enthusiastic professional jewelry artists and beaders and they work closely with the customers who usually become friends. Large open workspace and a private classroom/party room also. Their goal is to be able to supply anything a beader would need as well as a huge selection of beads from anywhere beads are produced. All kinds of beads, charms, findings, books and tools. If you can't make it into the store, be sure to order their video catalog.

GIFTS OF AVALON

1025 West University Avenue
Gainesville, FL 32601
Phone: 904-377-6225 /800-337-3844
FAX: 904-377-6860
Hours: Mon-Sat 10-6 Sun 12-5
Owner: Trude Tortorelli and
  Rhonda Bergman
Specialty: Japanese delica beads

Payment: Cks-MC-Visa-Discover
Retail: Yes
Wholesale: Quantity discounts
Mail Order: Yes
Catalog: $1 refundable
Classes: Call for schedule
Restringing: Call for quote
Custom Work: Call for quote

Located three blocks from the University of Florida, this is a full service bead store offering a wide range of seed beads (22° charlottes, 11°, 3-cuts), plus thousands of varieties of beads from all over the world sold by the piece, bag or strand. Also all types of cords, tools, findings, books and polymer clay. Workspace available and the staff will assist in design. Ready made jewelry and some gift items such as cards, candles, wind chimes and dream catchers.

POPPA BURKE'S TRADING POST

P. O. Box 552
432 S. 8th Street
Fernandina Beach, FL 32034
Phone: 904-261-8980
FAX: 904-261-9053
Hours: Mon-Sat 10-6
  Closed Wed. Sun 1-5
Owner: Brenda Hartley

Payment: Cks-MC-Visa
Retail: Yes
Wholesale: Kilo discounts on
  11o Czech seed beads
Mail Order: Yes
Catalog: $1 refundable
Classes: Call for schedule
Restringing: Yes

Reminiscent of an 18th-century trading post. A bead, book and body shop, where you can stretch your creativity, enhance your mind and soothe your body. Seed beads from sizes 8° to 22°, trade beads, Czech glass, rare and unusual beads of stone and amber, findings, beading supplies, primitive art and craft supplies, beadwork, herbal remedies, and authentic North American Indian art. Special orders for leather dresses, shirts, moccasins and beadwork.

WORLDBEADS

3098 A Fuller Street
Coconut Grove
Miami, FL 33133
Phone: 305-445-6060
Hours: Mon-Sat 10-9 Sun 10-6
Owner: Beadworks Canada

Payment: Cks-MC-Visa
Retail: Yes
Wholesale: Yes
Mail Order: Yes
Classes: Call for schedule
Restringing: Yes
Finished Pieces: Yes

Create your own accessories shop. Large selection of quality beads, findings, leather, books and more.

WORLDBEADS

321 N. University Dr. P-5, 3rd Flr.
Fashion Mall at Plantation
Plantation, FL 33324
Phone: 305-424-3111
Hours: Mon-Sat 10-9 Sun 10-6

Payment: Cks-MC-Visa
Retail: Yes
Wholesale: Yes
Mail Order: Yes
Classes: Call for schedule
Restringing: Yes

WORLDBEADS

18703-B Biscayne Boulevard
Aventura, FL 33180
Phone: 305-936-9777
Hours: Mon-Sat 10-9 Sun 10-6
Owner: Beadworks Canada

Payment: Cks-MC-Visa
Retail: Yes
Wholesale: Yes
Mail Order: Yes
Classes: Call for schedule
Restringing: Yes

Large selection of quality beads, findings, leather, books and more.

THE BEAD SHOPPE AT FORGE MILL CROSSING

102 Forge Mill Crossing
Morganton, GA 30560
Phone: 706-374-5074
FAX: 706-374-2290
Hours: Tues-Thurs 10:30-6
  Fri-Sat 10:30-9 Sun 11-5
Owner: Judi Sikes
Specialty: Old world trade beads

Payment: Cks-MC-Visa
Retail: Yes
Classes: Call for schedule
Restringing: Yes
Finished Pieces: Yes
Consignment: Call for details
Gallery: Call for details

A new store with friendly one-on-one assistance in creating your own unique jewelry. Wonderful selection of beads from around the world including old world trade beads and many other unique beads as well as a large supply of jewelry findings.

BEADAZZLES

290 Hilderbrand Drive
Atlanta, GA 30328
Phone: 404-843-8606
Hours: Mon-Fri 10-5 Sat 10-4
Owner: Alice Walker
Specialty: Design assistance

Payment: Cks-MC-Visa
Retail: Yes
Mail Order: Yes
Restringing: Yes
Custom Work: Call for prices
Finished Pieces: Yes
Consignment: Call

An excellent selection of upscale and unusual beads. Their specialty is working with a customer to create jewelry to go with a specific outfit. They also make a lot of bridesmaids earrings for weddings and will redesign and recreate and update your beaded jewelry. Also lots of findings, and ready made jewelry.

The size of beads can vary in a strand or between strands. Too great a size variation may not be desirable for beads used in making jewelry. Before buying beads make sure they are uniform in size.

DAL-CRAFT, INC.

P. O. Box 61
Tucker, GA 30085-0061
Phone: 800-521-7311
FAX: 404-939-2070
Hours: Mon-Fri 9-5
Owner: Emil J. Dalbo

Payment: Cks-M.O.
Retail: No
Mail Order: Upon request
Catalog: Free
See the color insert for a photo of the bead tray

Specialty: LoRan Bead Accessories designed to simplify working with and sorting and storing beads, findings and more.

Dal-Craft, Inc. is the manufacturer of LoRan Bead Accessories which include the following: Bead Tray, a six compartment bead project tray with lids for each compartment. (Compartment design ensures quick pick-up and threading of beads) Bead & Big Caddies, bead storage containers featuring individual compartments with individual tops, and the see-thru design; Bead Nabber, a magical seed bead tool that picks up seed beads with a touch. Check with your local bead store or send for the free Bead Accessory catalog.

HAWAII

A LITTLE CRAFT

619 Kapahulu Avenue
Honolulu, HI 96815
Phone: 808-732-0888
FAX: 808-732-0887
Hours: Mon-Fri 10-6 Sat 10-5 Sun 11-4
Owner: Aaron Chau

Payment: Cks-MC-Visa
Retail: Yes
Designer Discount: Yes

Specializing in personal service for novices and professionals and only five minutes from Waikiki . A variety of beads including antique, German glass, Venetian, Czech, handblown glass beads, seed and ceramic. Also semiprecious stones, carvings, crystal findings, cast pewter earring findings and Jade accent pieces and assistance available to help you create your own jewelry designs.

You can never have enough beads!

DACS BEADS

1320 Kalani Street, #201
Honolulu, HI 96817
Phone/FAX: 808-842-7714
Hours: Mon-Fri 10-6 Sat 9-5
Owner: Alethia Donathan
Specialty: Wide selection of old and new glass beads

Payment: Cks-MC-Visa
Retail: Yes
Wholesale: Yes
Mail Order: $100 minimum
Catalog: Free
Classes: Call for schedule

Hawaii's largest supplier of beads and findings located in beautiful Oahu. An extensive and unique supply of beads from the world over. When the owner travels she always looks for rare one-of-a-kind merchandise.   The store has a "bead happy" environment, an enclosed workshop with a variety of classes, lots of jewelry samples and source materials to inspire designers. Their main inventory is glass beads from all over the world.

THE FANTASY WORKS

2589 Kokomo Road
(call for driving directions)
Haiku, Maui, HI 96708
Phone/FAX: 808-572-1001
Hours: Mon, Tues, Thurs 9-8
   Fri 2-6   Sun 9-8
Owner: Susan Wolf
Specialty: Glass and stone beads

Payment: Cks
Retail: Yes
Wholesale: $200 minimum
Mail Order: Yes
Classes: By appointment
Restringing: Call
Custom Work: Call for quote
Finished Pieces: Yes
Consignment: Call for details

Located on the forest edge in Kokomo on Maui.   Vast selection of over 2,000 kinds of beads, findings in sterling silver and gold filled, leather, wire, stringing supplies and tools. Discounts for quantity purchases and 10% off to bead society members on proof of membership. Also finished work at wholesale prices and free advice given.

Millefiore is a tubular bead with intricate floral patterns, formed by tiny disks of mosaic glass embedded in the glass core.

MOUNTAIN MAN INDIAN TRADING CO. & BEADROOM

504 Bank Street
Wallace, ID 83873
Phone: 208-752-8671
FAX: 208-752-9411
Hours: Mon-Sat 9-5
  Call for winter hours
Owner: Dave and Chris Rust

Payment: Cks-MC-Visa
Retail: Yes
Mail Order: Yes
Classes: Open schedule
Restringing: Call for prices
Custom Work: Call for quote
Finished Pieces: Yes

Specialty: Handcrafted items from mountain people and Native Americans.

Unique handmade items from mountain people and Native Americans. Also artifacts, pottery, cards, jewelry, and t-shirts.

7 TRUMPETS BEAD STUDIO

1607 Third Street
Coeur d'Alene, ID 83814
Phone/FAX: 208-765-0755
Hours: Mon-Fri 10-5:30 Sat 10-2
Owner: Jane Cooper
Specialty: Unique beads

Payment: Cks-MC-Visa
Retail: Yes
Wholesale: $30 minimum
Mail Order: $25 minimum
Classes: By appointment
Restringing: Call
Custom Work: Call for quote
Finished Pieces: Yes

Full range of beads from around the world and beading supplies.

ZIZZYZAZA BEAD & EMBELLISHMENT EMPORIUM

Mail: 2709 N. 8th Street
Store: 1307 (rear) Best Avenue
Coeur d'Alene, ID 83814
Phone/FAX: 208-765-6758
Hours: Tues-Sat 12-5
Owner: Lisa Hobson

Payment: Cks
Retail: Yes
Wholesale: Yes
Mail Order: Yes
Classes: Call for schedule
Finished Pieces: Yes

Exhibiting at: InterMountain Bead Bazaar, July 2, 1995; Coeur d'Alene, Bead Festival November 1995. Call for locations.

Many styles of beads: 3 cuts, Czech, Indian, wood and metal as well as gifts, charms, fabric, fiber, books, magazines and finished jewelry. The shop is a little hard to find so call for directions. If they don't have what you want, they will try their best to find it or send you to the nearest bead store that does so you can see all the local stores.

BEAD IN HAND

145 Harrison
Oak Park, IL 60304
Phone: 708-848-1761
Hours: Mon-Fri 10-6
  Sat 10-5   Sun 1-5

Payment: Cks-MC-Visa
Retail: Yes
Classes: Call for schedule
Restringing: Yes
Finished Pieces: Yes
Consignment: Call for details

Owners: Renee Carswell and Doris Weinbaum
Exhibiting at: Midwest Bead Society bazaar, Evanston.

Large assortment of beads from all over the world, all the supplies needed to make jewelry and beaded items, tools, books and ethnic pieces. Classes in jewelry making and beadmaking (with special rates for non-profit groups). Birthday parties available where guests can make polymer beads to create a finished necklace or design jewelry from beads in the store. Also glass beadmaking demonstrations and a youth holiday bead craft bazaar.

BEAD IT!

5242 N. Clark Street
Chicago, IL 60640
Phone: 312-561-9683
Hours: Tues-Sat 11-6 Sun 12-4
Owners: Donna and Gwen Kato

Payment: Cks-MC-Visa
Retail: Yes
Classes: Call for schedule
Restringing: Yes
Custom Work: Call for prices
Finished Pieces: Yes

A resource for beaders of all levels with a variety of beads and high quality findings. They feature beads from contemporary glass and polymer clay artists. Polymer clay and lampworking demonstrations help strengthen and introduce these art forms. They believe it is important to touch beads in order to appreciate their beauty and have arranged the store to reflect this. Books and instruction booklets featuring Cernit and Sculpey, self-published by Prairie Craft Co. and Donna Kato.

TIP: "Nymo is my thread of choice for bead embroidery and beadweaving. After reeling off the desired length, I stretch it by pulling hard in opposite directions on the ends. This removes the curl which causes tangles and improves the tension of my work." Robin Atkins, Beads Indeed!, Seattle, WA.

THE BEAD LADY

101 Devonshire Drive, Suite H
Champaign, IL 61820
Phone/FAX: 217-352-0932
Hours: Mon-Fri 12-7 Sat 10-5
   Closed Tuesday and Sunday
Owner: Carol Jo Morgan

Payment: Cks-MC-Visa
Retail: Yes
Classes: Call for schedule
Restringing: Call for quote
Custom Work: Call for prices
Finished Pieces: Yes
Specialty: Education

Wide variety of beads; clay, ceramic, cinnabar, silver, Austrian crystals, copper, Czech, seed, bugles, pearls, porcelain, brass, and more. The old and collectible to the unusual or modern, gathered from around the world. Also, findings, books, tools, threads, custom designs, advice and bead identification. "Used" beads bought.

BEADAZZLED, A BEAD EMPORIUM

2002 Central Street
Evanston, IL 60201
Phone: 708-864-9494
Hours: Mon-Fri 10-7 Sat 10-5
   Sun 12-4
Owner: Mary Lee Inman
Specialty: Personal service

Payment: Cks-MC-Visa
Retail: Yes
Classes: Call for schedule
Restringing: $10 per strand
Custom Work: $20 and up
Finished Pieces: Yes

A hands-on bead store offering friendly advice and a work table with all the necessary tools available free for everyone to use. Minor repair work is usually completed the same day. Birthday parties for children and adults, a great findings department, books, tools, you name it, they have it. A huge assortment of glass beads, lampwork, handmade and one-of-a-kind beads from all over the world. **Discount coupon in back of the Directory.**

THE BEADHIVE

227 S. Third Street
Geneva, IL 60134
Phone: 708-232-3866
Hours: Mon-Thurs 10-5:30
   Fri 10-8 Sat 10-5:30 Sun 12-4
Owners: Leslie Owings and Jean Narimatsu
Specialty: Personal service

Payment: Cks-MC-Visa
Retail: Yes
Classes: Call for schedule
Restringing: $5- $15
Custom Work: Call for prices
Gallery: Call for details

Create your own bead designs in a leisure cozy environment with free basic instruction. Beads from around the world span the years from the African trade to the latest in Fimo from four talented artists. Sterling and 14k gold findings, cording from satin to leather, parties, gift certificates, kits, books, tools, and the Beadhive bonus plan.

BODACIOUS BEADS

1942 River Road
Des Plaines, IL 60018
Phone/FAX: 708-699-7959
Hours: Tues 10-8 Wed-Sat 10-6
Owner: Judith Schwab
Specialty: Wide variety

Payment: Cks-MC-Visa
Retail: Yes
Classes: Call for schedule
Restringing: Yes
Custom Work: Call for prices
Finished Pieces: Yes
Consignment: Call for details
Gallery: For local bead artists

Exhibiting at: All local retail shows, call for exact dates.

All kinds of beads from all over the world and all the stringing supplies you'll need to create your own unique designs. Low prices and volume discounts. Beads by the string and the hank and a discount to member s of the Bead Society of Greater Chicago.

CARAVAN BEADS

3350 N. Paulina
Chicago, IL 60657
Phone: 312-248-9555
FAX: 312-248-9594
Hours: Mon-Wed 11-7 Thurs 11-9
  Fri 11-7 Sat 11-6 Sun 12-5
Owners: Daniel and Charlene Steele
Specialty: Great beads

Payment: Cks-MC-Visa
Retail: Yes
Classes: Call for schedule
Restringing: Call for quote
Custom Work: Call for prices
Finished Pieces: Yes

Exhibiting at: Chicago Midwest Bead Society sales, call for dates

A large selection of beads from around the world, findings, supplies to make your own jewelry, books, magazines and tools. In-store work table with fre use of tools where customers can sit and make their jewelry and the staff is happy to help. Private parties and birthday parties available.

DA BEADS

547 North Euclid
Oak Park, IL 60302
Phone: 708-386-6542
FAX: 312-939-0664
Hours: By appointment only
Owners: Jon, Nita and Brett Kubricht
Specialty: Porcelain beads from Bulgaria and ethnic beads

Payment: Cks
Retail: Yes
Wholesale: $50 minimum
Mail Order: $50 minimum
Catalog: $4 and resale no.
Finished Pieces: Yes

Exhibiting at: Chicago Midwest Bead Society sales, Born to Bead Shows and Bead Society of Greater Chicago sales, call for dates.

Selling, by appointment only, a unique variety of ethnic beads from Indonesia, sterling silver and porcelain beads from Bulgaria and their own jewelry called J-Ropes. Order the catalog for more details.

INTERNATIONAL BEADTRADER

499 Pennsylvania Avenue
Glen Ellyn, IL 60137
Phone: 708-545-0628
Hours: Call
Manager: Phil Reno
Specialty: All kinds of beads

Payment: Cks-MC-Visa
Retail: Yes
Wholesale: Yes
Mail Order: Yes
Catalog: $5 refundable
Classes: Call for schedule
Restringing: Call for prices

Exhibiting at: Chicago Midwest Bead Society sales.

A direct importer of a large selection of beads from around the world.
Findings and bead supplies for beginners and designers as well as
books, tools, supplies and findings.

INTERNATIONAL BEADTRADER

6 S. Northwest Highway   **Payment**: Cks-MC-Visa
Park Ridge, IL 60068   **Retail**: Yes
Phone: 708-692-9905   **Wholesale**: Yes
Hours: Call   **Mail Order**: Yes
Owner: Bonnie Moore   **Catalog**: $5 refundable
Specialty: All kinds of beads   **Classes**: Call for schedule
Exhibiting at: Chicago Midwest Bead Society sales.

A direct importer of a large selection of beads from around the world. Findings and bead supplies for beginners and designers as well as books, tools, supplies and findings.

ORIGINALS GALLERY OF ANTIQUE JEWELRY AND BEADS

1020 Davis   **Payment**: Cks-MC-Visa
Evanston, IL 60201   **Retail**: Yes
Phone: 708-328-4040   **Classes**: Call for schedule
Hours: Tues-Sat 11:30-5:30   **Restringing**: $18 minimum
Owner: Naomi Rubin   **Custom Work**: $18 minimum
Specialty: High quality beads   **Consignment**: Antique only
Exhibiting at: Chicago Midwest Bead Society sale, Nov. 12, 1995

Selection of romantic jewelry from ages past or inspired adornments of your own design. Also findings, components, stringing materials and tools.

QUEEN BEADS

2028 W. Cortez   **Payment**: Cks
Chicago, IL 60622   **Retail**: Yes
Phone: 312-252-6013   **Wholesale**: Yes
FAX: 312-549-0063   **Mail Order**: Yes
Hours: By appointment only   **Catalog**: Yes
    Finished Pieces: Yes
Owners: Gina Lambert and Laurie Haughey
Specialty: Japanese Delica and 'E' beads wholesale in tubes

Importer of Japanese delica and 'E' beads and Japanese glass and glass rods for beadmaking. They are also glass beadmakers using Italian and Japanese glass and jewelry designers who customize their pieces to each customers taste.

THE BEAD WORKSHOP
2222 Mishawaka Avenue
South Bend, IN 46615
Phone: 219-237-0500
Hours: Tues-Fri 11-6 Sat 10-5
Owner: Steve Ross

Payment: Cks-MC-Visa
Retail: Yes
Classes: Call for schedule
Finished Pieces: Yes
Consignment: Yes

The largest bead store in Indiana with beads from around the world, findings, Fimo beadmaking supplies, books and tools. Workspace available and assistance available in creating your own jewelry.

JUST BEADS
P. O. Box 456
328 State Road 144
Bargersville, IN 46106
Phone: 317-422-5006
FAX: 317-422-9202
Hours: Mon and Wed 1-4
Owners: Terri Brown and
  Carolyn Dresslar
Specialty: Seed beads and classes

Payment: Cks-MC-Visa
Retail: Yes
Wholesale: $100 minimum
Mail Order: $25 minimum
Catalog: Yes
Classes: Call for schedule
Finished Pieces: Yes
Consignment: Yes

Exhibiting at: Bead Society of Greater Chicago and Ohio Bead Society sales. Call for dates and locations

All kinds of beads, seed, foil-glass, semiprecious, ceramic, hex, *delica* and antique. Fetishes (American Indian and Hong Kong), books, videos, findings, porcupine quills, turquoise and silver jewelry.

UNIQUE CREATIONS
323 - 10th Avenue North
Clinton, IA 52732
Phone: 319-242-4325
Hours: By appointment only
Owners: Gary and Alice Lauber

Payment: Cks-MC-Visa
Retail: Yes
Mail Order: Yes
Catalog: Available soon

Specialty: All kinds

Large selection of beads in many styles, shapes and colors including Czech glass, foil, India glass, Austrian crystal, Miracle beads; hand-woven dream catchers and many other unique and unusual pieces. Collectors and designers will find this store a valuable resource for new and exciting items.

bodacious beads

large selection
small prices

1942 river road
des plaines, ill. 60018
(708) 699-7959

Tues. 10 a.m.–8 p.m.
Wed.–Sat. 10 a.m.–6 p.m.
judith schwab

near o'hare airport and major expressways

KANSAS

INTERNATIONAL BEADTRADER

1017-1/2 Massachusetts
Lawrence, KS 66044
Phone: 913-865-4181
Hours: Call
Manager: Carol Collier
Specialty: All kinds of beads

Payment: Cks-MC-Visa
Retail: Yes
Wholesale: Yes
Mail Order: Yes
Catalog: $5 refundable
Classes: Call for schedule

A direct importer of a large selection of beads from around the world. Findings and bead supplies for beginners and designers. Also books, tools, supplies and findings.

INTERNATIONAL BEADTRADER

3700 E. Douglas #80A
Clifton Square
Wichita, KS 67208
Phone: 316-688-4444
Hours: Call
Specialty: All kinds of beads

Payment: Cks-MC-Visa
Retail: Yes
Wholesale: Yes
Mail Order: Yes
Catalog: $5 refundable
Classes: Call for schedule

A direct importer of a large selection of beads from around the world. Findings and bead supplies for beginners and designers. Also books, tools, supplies and findings.

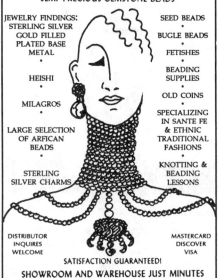

84

THE BEADIN' PATH
86B Main Street
Yarmouth, ME 04096
Phone: 207-846-4151
Hours: Tues-Sat 10-6 Sun 1-5
Owner: Jan Parker

Payment: Cks-MC-Visa
Retail: Yes
Wholesale: $30 minimum
Mail Order: Yes
Catalog: Free
Restringing: Call for prices
Finished Pieces: Yes

Quaint bead shop in picturesque small town. Beads are displayed in old print type drawers for easy access and viewing. A large selection of a variety of beads, semi-precious, vintage glass, Bali silver, handblown glass, castings and Fimo. Also books, tools, leather, findings, and anything else you need. They'll try to find what you want if they don't have it. A great selection of ready made jewelry, sterling rings, earrings and crystal pendants and kits.

CARAVAN BEADS, INC.
449 Forest Avenue
Forest Avenue Plaza
Portland, ME 04101
Phone: 207-761-2503
FAX: 207-874-2664
Hours: Mon-Sat 10-6 Thurs 10-8 Sun 1-5
Specialty: Very well stocked store
Owners: Barry and Jean Kahn and Carolyn and Joe Mitchell

Payment: Cks-MC-Visa-AE
Retail: Yes
Wholesale: Yes
Finished Pieces: Yes

The largest supply of beads and beading supplies in Maine. Worktables, tools and staff help customers design and make jewelry. Direct importers of Greek ceramic beads and leather. Beads include fancy shapes, seed, wood, base metal castings, Fimo, antique Czech and German glass, art glass, African and Chinese porcelain. They also offer consulting service to clients wishing to open retail bead stores around the country. In 1994 they helped clients open six stores including their licensee in Chicago. Licensing arrangements available in many states.

ACCENTS BEAD SHOP
4930 Hampden Lane
Bethesda, MD 20814
Phone: 301-656-7307
FAX: 301-657-8305
Hours: Mon-Sat 10-5 Thurs 10-7
Owners: Nancy and Milt Criswell
Specialty: Beads and findings

Payment: Cks-MC-Visa
Retail: Yes
Wholesale: $75 minimum
Mail Order: $75 minimum
Catalog: $2
Classes: Call for schedule
Restringing: Yes
Gallery Space: Yes

Exhibiting at: Washington D.C. Bead Society Bazaars, spring and fall. Call for dates and locations of other bazaars.

A one-stop shopping center with an exceptionally large selection of beads, findings and Himalayan fine silver. A unique shopping experience and a "can't miss" visit for beaders in the Washington, D.C. area. Over 5,000 different beads from all over the world. Accents was described in a local newspaper as "part bead store, part museum and part mouth dropping awesome". Free parking and located near a Metro stop.

BEADAZZLED
501 North Charles Street
Baltimore, MD 21201
Phone: 410-837-2323
FAX: 301-608-0518
Hours: Mon-Sun 10:30-6
Owners: Penny and Erik
  Diamanti deWidt
Specialty: Quality beads

Payment: Cks-MC-Visa-AE
Retail: Yes
Mail Order: Yes
Catalog: $5
Classes: Call for schedule
Restringing: Yes
Gallery Space: Yes

Exhibiting at: Washington D.C. Bead Society Bazaars, spring and fall.

Beads of every sort from everywhere for collectors and beginners in this clean, well-lit, inspiring environment. Antique to contemporary, ethnic to classic, gemstones, glass, sterling, 14K, gold filled, brass, amber and even plastic. Seed beads, fetishes, amazing selection of strands, trade beads, Czech and Indian glass. Knowledgeable and helpful staff and free how-to handouts. Tools, wide selection of findings and stringing materials and the best selection of bead books ever assembled. Their goal is to help unleash your creativity through beads. Importing directly keeps the prices down.

BEADECKED

75 Maryland Avenue
Annapolis, MD 21401
Phone: 410-263-4601
Hours: Mon-Sat 10-5 Sun 11-5
Owner: Tom Olson

Payment: Cks-MC-Visa
Retail: Yes

Complete bead shop with jewelry, gifts and handcrafted items.

BEAD IT!

716 Dulaney Valley Road
Towson, MD 21204
Phone: 410-825-6177
FAX: 410-825-6178
Hours: Mon-Sat 10-5
Owners: Debbie Edlow
Specialty: Semi-precious glass beads

Payment: Cks-MC-Visa
Retail: Yes
Wholesale: Yes
Classes: Call for schedule
Restringing: Call for quote

A great selection of glass, semiprecious, plated beads, findings, tools and books. A wide range of seed bead colors and sizes are also available. The owners believe in a philosophy of total customer service.

BEADWORKS

905 South Ann Street
Baltimore, MD 21231
Phone: 410-732-BEAD
FAX: 410-732-2374
Hours: Daily. Call as hours change
   during summer and holidays
Owner: Bronwyn Thompson-Henry

Payment: Cks-MC-Visa
Retail: Yes
Classes: Call for schedule
Restringing: Yes
Custom Work: Yes
Finished Pieces: Yes
Consignment: Yes
Specialty: The unusual

Extraordinary collection of beads at affordable prices, findings, tools, books and great classes and instructors. Customer service and assistance are key to their philosophy with time and attention given always.

FANTASY BEADS

11254 Triangle Lane
Wheaton, MD 20902
Phone: 301-933-8411
Hours: Mon-Sat 11:30-6 Sun till 5
Owner: Gary Roman
Exhibiting at: Washington D.C. Bead Society Bazaars, spring and fall.

Payment: Cks-MC-Visa-AE
Retail: Yes
Wholesale: Yes
Mail Order: $25 minimum
Catalog: Free
Specialty: Great beads

All kinds of great beads including ancient, antique, Czech and Japanese seed beads, glass, findings, charms and a full range of bead merchandise. The catalog is limited so visit the store for the largest selection.

HURRICANE BEADS

1615 Sulgrave Avenue
Baltimore, MD 21209
Phone: 410-542-7499
Hours: Tues- Fri 12-6 Sat 12-5
Owners: Leora Goldman
Specialty: Vintage glass and sterling silver
Exhibiting at: International Fashion Exhibitions and the Whole Bead Show, call for current schedule.

Payment: Cks-MC-Visa
Retail: Yes
Wholesale: $500 minimum
Mail Order: $50 minimum
Catalog: Free
Classes: Call for information

Baltimore's first bead store is the most popular and has the largest inventory of any bead store in the mid-Atlantic region with piles of stuff. Don't expect to come in for a quick look. No designing in the store as there is no space since every inch is taken up with BEADS! Servicing many institutions, theatres, movies and other costuming needs as well as the jewelry trade. Also tools and other supplies.

MARVIN SCHWAB

2313 Distribution Circle
Silver Spring, MD 20910
Phone: 301-565-0487
FAX: 301-565-0489
Hours: Call for appointment
Owners: Marvin and Teresa Schwab
Specialty: Accent beads
Exhibiting at: International Gem and Jewelry shows, local bead bazaars and others, call for current schedule.

Payment: Cks-MC-Visa-AE
Retail: Yes
Wholesale: $30 minimum
Mail Order: $30 minimum
Catalog: $3 refundable
Finished Pieces: Yes

A full service for wholesale/retail beads, findings, tools and supplies. Working with all levels of buyers from distributors to crafters. They are direct importers from overseas with a constant flow of new and exciting merchandise. Consulting services available on how to start a bead store. Also faceted gemstones, sterling silver and gold-filled wire.

TIP: "Use small lined graph paper to chart your design before you start stringing beads. This helps visualize the design and dimensions of the project and can be used as a guide while stringing". Jill Jarkovsky, Bead Designer.

BEAD CONNECTION TOO

22 Grove Street
Wellesley, MA 02181
Phone: 617-235-2321
Hours: Tues-Sat 10-5:30 Sun 12-5
Owner: Marjorie R. Freiman
Specialty: Unique beads
Exhibiting at: Beadesigner
  International Bead Affaires

Payment: Cks-MC-Visa
Retail: Yes/$10 off after $100
Designer Discount: Beadesigner
  members receive discount
Mail Order: Yes
Classes: Call for information
Restringing: Call for quote
Finished Pieces: Yes
Consignment: Yes

The largest independent bead store between Boston and Providence. A large collection of semi-precious gems, plated and precious metal findings, tools, books and kits. Beads from all over the world including Czech glass, Austrian crystal, African trade, Venetian vintage glass, cloissone, sterling and gold-filled, letter beads (Fimo, ceramic, wood, glass and sterling) and all sorts of charms. A store with large work tables with tools, bead boards and assistance provided to help you design your own projects.

BEADNIKS (MORE THAN A BEAD STORE)

4 Church Street
Vineyard Haven, MA 02568
Phone: 508-693-7650
FAX: 508-693-7609
Hours: Winter Mon, Thurs-
  Sun 11-5 Summer 7 days 9-9
Owner: Sally McArthur
Specialty: Unusual beads

Payment: Cks-MC-Visa
Retail: Yes
Restringing: Yes
Custom Work: Yes
Finished Pieces: Yes

Located on Martha's Vineyard, a one-of-a-kind gem in the world of retail bead stores boasting a veritable treasure chest of beads and imported wares from Africa, China, Europe, South America and Southeast Asia. An ideal store for everyone, stocking an abundance of all different types of beads from seed beads to the most exotic antiques from afar. The staff is knowledgeable, courteous and will be happy to answer your questions and help you with your bead needs. Also artifacts and crafts from Southeast Asia.

BEADS ETC.

4 Mt. Vernon Street
Arlington, MA 02174
Phone: 617-646-1316
Hours: Tues- Sat 12-5
Owner: Roni McCall

Payment: Cks-MC-Visa
Retail: Yes
Wholesale: $25 minimum
Classes: Call for information
Restringing: $1 per inch
Finished Pieces: Yes

Exhibiting at: Beadesigner International Bead Affaire, call for dates.

Jewelry making supply store carrying semiprecious beads, charms, gold, silver and brass findings, ceramic, glass, cloisonne and seed beads. Also leather and silk cord, crystals, stringing supplies, books, tools, gift boxes, watch components, niobium coil and much more.

BEADWORKS

23 Church Street
Cambridge, MA 02138
Phone: 617-868-9777
FAX: 617-868-9229
Hours: Mon-Sat 10-8 Sun 12-6
Owner: Jessica Pollak

Payment: Cks-MC-Visa
Retail: Yes
Classes: Call for schedule
Restringing: $20 per hour
Finished Pieces: Yes

Located in Harvard Square, this store is a great destination for all visitors to the Boston area. A huge selection of all kinds of beads from ethnic to unusual, findings, books, tools and necklaces and earrings.

BEADWORKS

349 Newbury Street
Boston, MA 02115
Phone: 617-247-7227
FAX: 617-247-2322
Hours: Mon-Fri 11-7 Fri-Sat 10-8 Sun 12-6
Owner: Jessica Pollak

Payment: Cks-MC-Visa
Retail: Yes
Classes: Call for schedule
Restringing: $20 per hour
Finished Pieces: Yes

An enormous selection of all kinds of beads with plenty of room to put a project together, plus an extremely knowledgeable and cheerful staff to help. Also lots of contemporary lampworked glass beads.

CRYSTAL BLUE BEADING CO.

565 Mount Auburn Street, Ste. B
Watertown, MA 02172
Phone: 617-923-2337
Hours: Tues-Sat 11-6 Wed 11-9
Owner: Lisa G. Wolf
Specialty: Seed beads and
Czech glass beads

Payment: Cks-MC-Visa
Retail: Yes
Mail Order: Yes/No catalog
Classes: Call for schedule
Custom Work: Yes
Finished Pieces: Yes
Gallery Space: Yes
Consignment: Yes

Exhibiting at: Beadesigner International Bead Affaires, call for dates.

The seed-beader's paradise! A large collection of glass, seed, cut, bugle beads and much more. A friendly and knowledgeable staff; frequent free community beadcraft gatherings; frequent beader program; and a variety of beadwork and art shows. Enter the annual Rainforest Beadwork Contest every October (a benefit to contribute to rainforest awareness and preservation). Also music, large collection of bead books, videos (sales and rentals) and tools and supplies. **Discount Coupon in back of the Directory.**

THE PEAR TREE

1355 Beacon Street
Brookline, MA 02146
Phone: 617-277-9330
FAX: 617-277-9399
Hours: Mon-Sat 10-7 Sun 12-5
Owner: Rhona Hirschowitz
Contact: Thalia Tringo, Mgr.
Specialty: Ethnic and contemporary glass beads

Payment: Cks-MC-Visa-AE
Retail: Yes
Classes: Call for schedule
Restringing: $20 per hour
Finished Pieces: Yes

Handmade folk art from all over the world and a full line of beads, findings, and stringing materials. All kinds of beads from ethnic to contemporary to gemstones, glass, vintage and Fimo. Also textiles, cards, jewelry, pottery and instruments. **Discount Coupon in back of the Directory.**

SINGARAJA IMPORTS

P. O. Box 2321
Oak Bluffs, MA 02557
Phone: 508-693-4165
FAX: 508-693-4121
Hours: Call Mon-Fri
Owner: Jerry Visconti

Payment: MC-Visa-AE
Wholesale: $100 minimum
Mail Order: $100 minimum
Catalog: $3
Finished Pieces: Yes
Exhibiting at: many shows,
call for current schedule.

Direct importers of silver and glass beads from Southeast Asia. Also sells unusual components. Call for catalog.

Beadworks®

An Adventure in Creativity

Choose from over 3,500 types of glorious beads from all around the world.

Open Daily Call for Hours

905 South Ann Street
Ann Street Wharf
In Historic Fells Point
Baltimore, MD 21231
410.732.BEAD (2323)

THE STONEWORKS
Box 280
11 Pleasant Street
Dunstable, MA 01827
Phone: 508-649-6613
Hours: Tues-Fri 12-5 Thurs 12-8
  Call for Sat and Sun hours
Owners: Curt and Sandy Gates
Contact: Sandy Gates
Specialty: Beads made of native New England materials

Payment: Cks-MC-Visa
Retail: Yes
Wholesale: Yes
Mail Order: Yes
Classes: Call for schedule
Restringing: Yes
Custom Work: Yes
Finished Pieces: Yes

Friendly shop known for quality beads, wampum, gemstone beads, mineral specimens, tools and supplies at low prices. Frequent classes with a limit of three students ensures successful learning. GIA graduates provide expert gemological advice. Celebrating 22 years of business in an antique building by the village green.

TAVROS LEATHERWEAR, INC.

9 Tripp Street
Framingham, MA 01701
Phone: 508-820-4444
Phone: 800-8-TAVROS
FAX: 508-875-5820
Hours: Mon-Fri 9-6
Payment: Call
Retail: Call
Wholesale: Volume discounts
Mail Order: Yes
Catalog: Free

Owners: Vassilis and Margaret Kourbetis
Contact: Carolyn Laskey, Mgr.
Specialty: Natural leather cord from Greece
Exhibiting at: International Fashion Boutique shows, call for current schedule.

Tavros, in business 10 years, is a manufacturer, importer and wholesaler and is best known for its natural leather goods which darken with age. There are several retail locations and mail order catalogs. Their leather cord product is great and is sought after by artisans for its strength, color fastness and smooth round texture. The best 2mm leather cord at the best price is just a toll free call away. They can source any bead made in Greece.

THE WANDERING BULL, INC.

P. O. Box 1075
247 South Main Street
Attleboro, MA 02703
Phone: 508-226-6074
FAX: 508-226-4878
Hours: Mon-Fri 11-6 Wed 11-8
   Sat 10-5 Call for seasonal Sun hours
Payment: MC-Visa-Discover
Retail: Yes
Wholesale: $10 minimum
Mail Order: $5 minimum
Catalog: $2
Classes: Call for schedule

Owner: Andrew Bullock
Specialty: American Indian crafts and supplies
Exhibiting at: New England area PowWows, call for schedule.

A complete line of beads and accessories for Native American beadwork and related crafts. Included are seed beads, pony, Crow and metal beads. Also a complete selection of craft supplies for Indian regalia, needles, 600 book titles, leather, thread, looms and findings.

BEAD WORKS, INC.

32751 Franklin Road
Franklin, MI 48025
Phone: 810-855-5230
Hours: Tues-Wed-Fri-Sat 10-5
  Thurs 10-7
Owner: Ida Joyrich

Payment: Cks-MC-Visa
Retail: Yes
Wholesale: $100 minimum
Restringing: Yes
Custom Work: Yes
Finished Pieces: Yes

Tremendous selection of beads from around the world. Vintage, ethnic, semiprecious, Austrian, German, Czech and Japanese glass. The store is located in a 150 year old building in historic Franklin.

BIRMINGHAM BEAD STORE

154 W. Maple Road
Birmingham, MI 48009
Phone: 810-644-7609
FAX: 810-540-4114
Hours: Mon-Wed 10-5:30
  Thurs 10-8 Fri-Sat 10-5:30
Owner: Arlene Green
Specialty: Unique glass beads

Payment: Cks-MC-Visa-AE
Retail: Yes
Designer Discount: 20%
Restringing: Yes
Finished Pieces: Yes
Custom Work: Yes
Classes: Call for schedule

In the heart of Birmingham this mecca for designers and bead collectors has customers coming from all over the state. Established in 1974, the staff has a wonderful knowledge of the history of beads along with a very large inventory of old and new, rare and unusual beads. They sell old and new Czech crystal and glass, Austrian crystal, African and Dutch antique beads, seed, bugle beads, pearls, rhinestones, Venetian glass, pre-Columbian, lampworked glass beads, spiritual and cultural amulets, and other talisman pieces old and new.

TIP: "Your workspace can be as important as the materials used. Every beader has their own preference, but there are certain necessities that are common to all. A greal deal of physical pain in the back, shoulders, neck and wrist can be avoided with proper posture and position. Ample space is needed to insure freedom of movement and to make sure that threads do not get caught on items crammed into a tiny work space." *Earring Designs By Sig*, *Book II*, Sigrid Wynne-Evans.

CURRIE BEADS

218 State Street
St. Joseph, MI 49085
Phone: 616-982-1948
FAX: 616-983-5078
Hours: Mon-Sat 10-6 Sun 12-5
 (Sun hours during summer only)
Owner: Currie Butzbaugh
Specialty: Contemporary lampworked beads

Payment: Cks-MC-Visa
Retail: Yes
Mail Order: Yes
Classes: Call for schedule
Restringing: Yes
Custom Work: Yes
Finished Pieces: Yes

A cozy store with knowledgeable staff that will help with projects. Selling all kinds of beads from lampworked to African trade, vintage Bohemian, tools and much more. Books and magazines on site for reference and sale to encourage interest in bead history and identification. Work space available to all customers. Store overlooks Lake Michigan in the downtown shopping district of St. Joseph.

MICHIGAN LAPIDARY SUPPLY COMPANY

29845 Beck Road
Wixom, MI 48393
Phone/FAX: 810-624-8350
Hours: Mon-Fri 10-6 Sat 10-4
Owner: Virginia Williams
Contact: Gaye Tolliver

Payment: Cks-MC-Visa
Retail: Yes
Wholesale: $10 minimum
Mail Order: $10 minimum
Catalog: $1
Restringing: Yes

Lapidary supplies and equipment, including findings, cabochons, beads and beading supplies, metals, books, display cases, jewelry making supplies and tools, rough rock and tumbling supplies. Beads are mostly natural stone beads in various shapes and sizes and Swarovski crystal in 15 colors.

NOC BAY TRADING COMPANY

1133 Washington Avenue
P. O. Box 295
Escanaba, MI 49829-0295
Phone: 906-789-0505
FAX: 906-789-5619
Hours: Mon-Fri 10-5:30 Sat 10-3
Owner: Loren and Donna Woerpel
Specialty: Learning circle kits
Exhibiting at: Summer and fall pow-wows in Michigan and Wisconsin, call for current schedule.

Payment: Cks-MC-Visa
Retail: Yes
Wholesale: Yes
Mail Order: Yes
Catalog: $3
Custom Work: Yes
Finished Pieces: Yes

Mail order traders of beads, findings and all supplies needed for Native American dance clothing. Coffee is always on and customers are free to design their own projects. Friendly advice offered if needed.

PRIYA IMPORTS

7001 Orchard Lake Road, 412-D
West Bloomfield, MI 48322
Phone: 800-869-9240 or 810-861-3400
FAX: 810-851-3402
Hours: Tues-Fri 10-5 Sat 10-4

Payment: Cks-MC-Visa
Wholesale: Yes

Priya Imports sells gemstone and precious metal beads, old silver beads, pearls, findings and beading supplies.

MINNESOTA

BEAD IT!

383 West Market Place
Mall of America
Bloomington, MN 55425
Phone: 612-858-8612
Hours: Mon-Sat 10-9:30 Sun 11-7
Owner: Alessandra Scamardo
Specialty: Ethnic and Czech glass beads

Payment: Cks-MC-Visa
Retail: Yes
Wholesale: Yes
Mail Order: $25 minimum
Catalog : Call for price
Classes: Seasonal /Call
Restringing: Yes

Located in the Mall of America, the largest indoor mall in the United States. One of the largest selections of Czech and Japanese seed beads in the area. A wonderful selection of unusual beads and components from around the world, findings, tools, supplies, and lots of bead books. The staff will assist you with design and techniques.

THE BEAD MONKEY

4940 France Avenue South
Edina, MN 55410
Phone: 612-929-4032
Hours: Mon-Sun 10-6
Owner: Tina Agar

Payment: Cks-MC-Visa
Retail: Yes
Designer Discount: 20%
Restringing: Yes
Custom Work: Call for quote

All kinds of beads including antique German and Austrian glass, new Czech, semiprecious stones, unusual metal components, handmade glass beads and a large selection of strands are available at discount prices. Custom designing available.

BEAUTIFUL BEADS

115 Hennepin Avenue
Minneapolis, MN 55401
Phone: 612-333-0170
Hours: Sun 1-4 and by appt
Owner: Diane Fitzgerald
Specialty: European and Japanese glass beads

Payment: Cks
Retail: Yes .
Classes: Call for schedule

Glass, seed and other beads, supplies, books and classes in unusual bead assemblages. Diane is co-author with Helen Banes of the new book *Beads and Thread: A New Technique for Fiber Jewelry* and author of a new book about the techniques of creating a sea anemone bracelet and other books coming soon.

BIJOUX BEAD, INC.

1595 W. Hwy 36
Rosedale Mall, Store 290
Roseville, MN 55113
Phone: 612-636-9029
Hours: Mon-Fri 10-9 Sat 10-8 Sun 11-6
Owner: Helen Vagle

Payment: Local Cks-MC-Visa
Retail: Yes
Classes: Call for schedule
Restringing: Yes
Custom Work: Yes

Over 3,500 items including beads from around the world and all the findings to complete your bead projects. All displayed in an open setting for a pleasant shopping experience.

BOBBY BEAD

1608 W. Lake Street
Minneapolis, MN 55408
Phone: 612-824-8281
FAX: 612-824-7942
Hours: Mon-Fri 10-8 Sat 10-6
  Sun-12-6
Owner: Robert Sorenson
Specialty: Create your own jewelry

Payment: Cks-MC-Visa-AE
Retail: Yes
Wholesale: $20 minimum
Designer Discount: 20%
Mail Order: Yes
Classes: Call for schedule

The largest full line bead store in the upper Midwest. A comfortable, organized and well lit business catering to the professional designer and the beginning beader. Offering a wide variety of beads from around the world and handmade unique styles from local artists. Books and classes are available to teach and inspire more techniques and design ideas. Friendly helpful staff are ready to assist you and many items are available in bulk packs to offer you a quantity discount.

COSECHA DESIGNS

746 E. Mill Street
Wayzata, MN 55391-1753
Phone/FAX: 612-475-1945
Hours: Mon-Sat 10-6
Owner: Gayle and John Liman
Specialty: Unique ethnic beads

Payment: Cks-MC-Visa-AE
Retail: Yes
Designer Discount: 10%
Classes: Call for schedule
Finished Pieces: Yes
Gallery Space: Yes
Consignment: Yes

Cosecha Designs carries a wide range of ethnic beads, old and new glass, lampwork, wood, fancy beads and findings plus seed beads of all finishes. They have gallery space and carry folk art, ethnic clothing, jewelry and objects d'art. **See the color insert for a photo of some of the beads available at Cosecha.**

CREATIVE FIBERS

5416 Penn Avenue So.
Minneapolis, MN 55419
Hours: Mon-Wed 10-5:30
  Thurs 10-8 Fri 10-5:30 Sat 10-5
Phone: 612-927-8307
Owner: Lynn Hazelton
Specialty: Fiber art

Payment: Cks-MC-Visa-AE
Retail: Yes
Mail Order: Yes
Classes: Call for schedule

Supplies for fiber arts, weaving, knitting, spinning, dyeing, basketry, papermaking, felting and beading including everything from the basics to the unusual. Selling Japanese seed beads and *delicas*, German and Austrian crystals, soapstone and a wide selection of charms.

MISSOURI

B & J ROCK SHOP

14744 Manchester Road
Ballwin, MO 63011
Phone: 314-394-4567
FAX: 314-394-7109
Hours: Mon-Sat 10-5
Owner: Julie Kepner

Payment: Cks-MC-Visa
Retail: Yes
Wholesale: $50 minimum
Mail Order: $15 minimum
Catalog: $3

All types of beads, findings, cabochons, settings, books and bead supplies. Also beautiful natural minerals, crystals and fossils, silver and silversmith's supplies.

BEAD IT!

231 St. Louis Union Station
St. Louis, MO 63103
Phone: 314-231-6286
Hours: Mon-Thurs 10-9
  Fri-Sat 10-10 Sun 11-7
Owner: Alessandra Scamardo
Specialty: Gemstones and Czech

Payment: Cks-MC-Visa-AE
Retail: Yes
Mail Order: $25 minimum
Catalog: Call for price
Classes: Seasonal schedule
Finished Pieces: Yes
Gallery Space: Yes
Consignment: Yes

Located in St. Louis Union Station, the highly acclaimed renovated train station in downtown St. Louis. A large selection of Czech and Japanese seed beads, a wonderful selection of unusual beads, contemporary lampworked beads and components from around the world. A wide assortment of findings, tools, supplies and lots of books. The staff is happy to assist you with design and techniques.

INTERNATIONAL BEADTRADER

4135 Pennsylvania
Kansas City, MO 64111
Phone: 816-753-1565
Hours: Call
Contact: Karren Deibler
Specialty: Unique selection

Payment: Cks-MC-Visa
Retail: Yes
Wholesale: Yes
Catalog: $5
Classes: Call for schedule
Restringing: Call for quote

Direct importer of a wide variety of beads from all over the world. A vast selection of beads, findings, and supplies for all beaders.

TERRANEAN DESIGNS

1771 S. Fremont
Springfield, MO 65804
Phone: 417-889-2402
Phone: 800-280-2402
FAX: 417-887-7697
Hours: Mon 10-6 Tues-Fri 10-9
  Sat 10-6 Sun 12-5
Owner: Tim and Sherrill Phillips
Specialty: Glass beads

Payment: Cks-MC-Visa-AE
Retail: Yes
Wholesale: Yes
Mail Order: Yes
Classes: Every Monday
Restringing: $7.50 and up
Finished Pieces: Yes

Relaxed comfortable atmosphere with lots of work space for customers to design their own jewelry and a staff that will offer design assistance. A full service bead store with a huge selection of all types of beads including the owners' handmade lampworked beads.

VEON CREATIONS

3565 State Hwy V
Desoto, MO 63020
Phone/Fax: 314-586-5377
Owner: Veon Schunzel
Hours: Mon-Fri 11-7
  Sat by appointment
Specialty: How-to books

Payment: Cks-MC-Visa
Retail: Beads
Wholesale: Books and earrings
Mail Order: Yes
Catalog: $3
Free Catalog w/Resale #: Yes
Classes: By request only
Finished Pieces: Yes

Basically a mail order business with some in-store sales by appointment and sales at several Indian pow wows. Veon is the author and publisher of *Creative Beaded Earrings* Volumes 1 thru 4, and the originator of Picture Beaded Earrings. All kinds and sizes of seed and bugle beads, instruction books, Indian craft supplies and tools.

WHITE HEART TRADING POST

7329 Watson Road
Mackenzie Pointe Plaza
St. Louis, MO 63119
Phone: 314-832-2526
  or 800-838-2526
FAX: 314-832-4038
Hours: Tues-Sat 10-9 Sun 11-5
Owner: Vida McEndollar

Payment: Cks-MC-Visa-AE
Retail: Yes
Mail Order: Yes
Catalog: Call for cost
Restringing: $7.50 and up
Finished Pieces: Yes
Classes: Call for schedule

A store for the serious beader. The well trained staff with extensive knowledge of the products and techniques will work with each client. The largest selection of beads, gemstones, clay, glass, ceramic, gold filled, trade beads and the selection is constantly expanding. Also findings, clasps, watch parts, charms, supplies, tools, books and supplies used by rendezvous and pow-wow participants.

ZUMA BEACH BEAD CO.

6655 Delmar Boulevard
At the Market in the U-City Loop
St. Louis, MO 63130
Phone: 314-862-3345
FAX: 314-645-4314
Hours: Tues-Fri 11-6 Sat 10-7
Owners: Jamie and Angela Cane
Specialty: Glass beads and limited edition beads for the collector

Payment: Cks-MC-Visa-AE
Retail: Yes
Wholesale: $50 minimum
Mail Order: $50 minimum
Catalog: $2
Classes: Call for schedule
Restringing: Yes

A full-service retail and wholesale bead store, providing in-store design assistance to help you create one of-a-kind designs. The class schedule often features special guest artists with new techniques. The owners concentrate on the educational aspects of beadwork and often give presentations of their frequent travels to Kenya and on the importance of beads in the countries they visit.

MONTANA

FOUR WINDS INDIAN TRADING POST

Box 580
Highway 93 - 3 Mi. North of
St. Ignatius, MT 59865
Phone: 406-745-4336
Hours: Daily 10-5
Owner: Preston Miller
Specialty: Native American

Payment: Cks-MC-Visa-AE
Retail: Yes
Wholesale: Yes
Mail Order: Yes
Catalog: $3
Restringing: Yes
Custom Work: Yes

Montana's oldest Indian trading post. Located on the Confederated Salish and Kootenai Reservation. Old and new beads, Indian made crafts and old Indian related material.

OLD BOZEMAN BEADS

321 E. Main Street
Bozeman, MT 59715
Phone: 406-587-1175
Hours: Mon-Sat 9:30-6 Sun 12-4
Owner: Richard Crowle
Specialty: New and old collectible beads

Payment: Cks-MC-Visa-AE
Retail: Beads
Wholesale: $500 minimum
Mail Order: $25 minimum

Gifts, gallery and beads, Indian artifact replicas, and arts and crafts of Montana.

POWDER HORN TRADING POST

2052 Hwy 2 East
Kalispell, MT 59901
Phone: 406-752-6669
Orders only: 800-746-8540
Hours: Mon-Fri 9-6 Sat 9-5
Owner: Cindy and Bud Hartley
Specialty: Seed beads
Contact: Cindy Hartley

Payment: Cks-MC-Visa
Retail: Yes
Mail Order: $10 minimum
Catalog: SASE
Classes: Call for schedule
Finished Pieces: Yes

A traditional trading post located in northwest Montana stocking a large supply of seed and trade beads. Located next to two Indian reservations, they also carry a full line of pow wow notions such as hairbone pipe, leather, beading supplies, Indian crafts and antiques.

NEBRASKA

INTERNATIONAL BEADTRADER

1637 P Street, #B
Lincoln, NE 68508
Phone: 402-438-2828
Hours: Call
Contact: Rita Jarvis, manager
Specialty: Unique selection

Payment: Cks-MC-Visa
Retail: Yes
Wholesale: Yes
Catalog: $5
Classes: Call for schedule
Restringing: Call for quote

Direct importer of a wide variety of beads from all over the world. A vast selection of beads, findings, and supplies for the beginning beader, jewelry designer, or retailer.

BEADS PLUS
4750 W. Sahara St. #13
Sahara Pavillion
Las Vegas, NV 89102
Phone: 702-259-6100
FAX: 702-259-6900
Hours: Mon-Sat 10-6 Sun 11-5
Owner: Joni Mann

Payment: Cks-MC-Visa-AE
Retail: Beads
Wholesale: Yes
Mail Order: Yes

All kinds of beads, leather, findings, watch parts, charms, tools and books. Friendly shop and staff will provide assistance in designing your own custom made jewelry. Just minutes from the Las Vegas strip, a great bead paradise get-away.

BEAUTY AND THE BEADS
402-A North Curry
Carson City, NV 89703
Phone: 702-887-1377
FAX: 702-883-0756
Hours: Tues-Sat 11-6
Owner: Gloria Lee

Payment: Cks-MC-Visa-AE
Retail: Yes
Wholesale: Yes
Mail Order: Yes
Classes: Call for information

This artist-owned business has a huge variety of all kinds of beads and centerpieces from all over the world. Lots of assistance to help you create your masterpieces. An extensive polymer clay bead collection and handmade gifts from around the world. A fun and crazy store where you're sure to have lots of fun. Drop by on your way to Reno or Tahoe, it's worth the stop.

LOVE-'R'-BEADS
4250 S. Rainbow Blvd, #1004-BD
Las Vegas, NV 89103
Phone: 702-252-7404
FAX: 702-252-0671
Hours: Mon-Fri 10-7 Sat 10-6
Owners: Doug Paddock and
    Cecil and Diana Ferguson

Payment: Cks-MC-Visa
Retail: Yes
Wholesale: Yes
Mail Order: Yes
Classes: Call for schedule
Restringing: Call for quote
Custom Work: Call for quote
Specialty: Great selection

A great bead store featuring thousands of beads from around the world, fine gemstones and pearls, all types of glass, findings, books, tools and supplies. Great prices on beads, a well stocked store worth the visit. Designer and resale discounts available.

SUGARPINE TRADING COMPANY

P. O. Box 18461
Reno, NV 89511
Phone: 702-849-3630
Hours: By appointment
Owner: Kimberly Lenz
Specialty: Artifacts suitable for jewelry and rare beads

Payment: Cash-Cks
Retail: Yes
Wholesale: Yes
Mail Order: Yes
Restringing: Yes
Custom Work: Yes
Finished Pieces: Yes

Exhibiting at: Northern California Bead Society bazaars, Tucson Gem Show and others. Call for current schedule.

A wholesale and retail bead and jewelry business specializing in the rare and unusual at reasonable prices. No catalog or price list because the inventory is one-of-a-kind. Collectable, unusual, rare, old, antique, and ancient handmade beads. They buy, trade and sell interesting antique jewelry and beads. If you have jewelry or beads to sell, send information including photos and asking price to the address above.

SUPPLIES 4 LESS

13001 Las Vegas Blvd. South
Las Vegas, NV 89124-9519
Phone: 702-361-3600
FAX: 702-896-9488
Hours: Wed-Sat 10-4
Owner: Phyllis Leon
Specialty: Costume jewelry supplies

Payment: Cks-MC-Visa-AE
Retail: Yes
Wholesale: Discounts
Mail Order: Yes
Catalog: $3.50

Limited hours for the public to buy at their outlet. Beads from all over the world, ladies' hats and supplies to decorate them with, memory wire, bolo supplies and a huge variety of craft supplies.

SWEETWATER TRADE CO.

4501 Kyle Drive
Wellington, NV 89444
Phone: 702-266-4081
Hours: Mon-Sun 8-5
Owners: Sandra McCormick and Larry Wahrenbrock

Payment: Checks
Retail: Yes
Wholesale: $200 minimum
Mail Order: $10 minimum
Catalog: $1 and LSASE
Finished Pieces: Yes

Specialty: Glass beads and handmade concho belts
Exhibiting at: Arizona Bead Bazaar, winter only, Tyson Wells Quartzsite, end of June and 1st week of February.

A traveling store that sells at 1840s Living History Events, craft shows and powwows. All crafts are authenticated and of the highest quality. Also seed, pony, Crow, French, and handmade ceramic beads. Collectors for the past 25 years, their catalog is constantly expanding.

THE BEADY EYE

12 West #7
Keene, NH 03431
Phone: 603-357-2323
Hours: Tues-Sat 10-5:30 Sun 12-4
Owner: Heather Avery
Specialty: Fimo beads

Payment: Cks-MC-Visa
Retail: Yes
Wholesale: $100 min. kits only
Designer Discount: Yes
Mail Order: Yes
Classes: Call for schedule
Restringing: Call for quote

A small and personal shop. Heather is also a craftsperson and makes a line of bead kits and she is generally on hand at all times to offer assistance with questions and design. Emphasis is on the craft of beadwork. Many one-of-a-kind beads from Czech to German art glass, lots of Fimo, gemstone, almost no plastic and art-to-wear jewelry.

CARAVAN BEADS OF NORTH CONWAY

Rt. 16, Main Street
Across from the train station
North Conway, NH 03860
Phone: 603-356-7608
Hours: Mon-Sun 10-6
Owner: Leigh Grady

Payment: Cks-MC-Visa
Retail: Yes
Wholesale: Yes
Classes: Call for schedule
Finished Pieces: Yes

A lovely shop in North Conway Village. A large selection of beads and beading supplies and gorgeous finished jewelry. Worktable and tools for customer use and employees are available to help with design. Beads from around the world including Czech, Japanese, African trade and much more. Gotta see it to believe it.

THE FIBER STUDIO

P. O. Box 637
9 Foster Hill Road
Henniker, NH 03242
Phone: 603-428-7830
Hours: Tues-Sat 10-4
  Sunday by chance
Owner: Pamela Grob
Specialty: Ethnic beads and fiberarts

Payment: Cks-MC-Visa
Retail: Yes
Catalog: Yarn catalog $4
Catalog: Fiber catalog $4
  no bead catalog
Classes: Yes
Finished Pieces: Yes

Beads from around the world and a large selection of findings and books on beads and the fiber arts. A variety of hand dyed unusual fibers; mohairs, silks chenilles, wool, cottons; spinning fibers, looms and wheels. Many classes on Fimo, bead stringing and fiber.

MAD AS A HATTER

10 Chestnut Street #2303
Exeter, NH 03833
Phone: 603-772-7879
Hours: By appointment, call
Owner: Kim DeNunzio
Specialty: Custom bead kits

Payment: Cks-MC-Visa
Retail: Yes
Wholesale: $50 minimum
Catalog: Free
Classes: Call for schedule
Finished Pieces: Yes

Be your own jewelry artisan with Kim's bead kits. Create a beautiful array of individual and distinctive personal adornments. The kits contain an assortment of beads which offer an endless variety of bead combinations. Each kit includes beads, findings and instructions to create an imaginative necklace, bracelet or pair of earrings. Also original affordable handcrafted jewelry using eclectic material combinations and various beads with an ethnic and contemporary flavor.

OVERSEAS MINING VENTURES, INC.

1 Merrill Drive, Suite 18
Hampton, NH 03842
Phone: 603-926-9266, 800-258-0853
FAX: 603-926-4499
Hours: Mon-Fri 9-5
Owner: Dallas Davenport

Payment: Cks
    MC-Visa-AE (Only in person)
Wholesale: $50 minimum
Mail Order: $50 minimum

Dallas operates seven mines overseas where they mine four colors of jade, blue chalcedony, chrome quartz and obsidian (3 colors). The rock is containerized in their yard in Istanbul and sent via cargo ship to the U.S. In the warehouse they maintain stocks of 30-60 metric ton of rough. They cut the rough open stones in the warehouse and sell it to lapidaries around the world. **See the color insert for a photo of the beads.**

TRACEY'S

1 Lafayette Terrace
North Hampton, NH 03862
Phone: 603-964-2323
FAX: 603-436-3756
Hours: Wed-Fri 10-6 Sat 11-7 Sun 12-5
Owner: Judy Tracey
Specialty: Lampworked beads

Payment: Cks-MC-Visa
Retail: Yes
Classes: Call for information

A retail bead store carrying beads of all kinds, kits, tools, semiprecious stones, instructional books and findings. There is a lampworking studio at the store where handmade glass beads are made and demonstrations are given. Their Bead Club entitles you to discounts, freebies and access to the video library.

THE BEAD STAMPEDE
54 West Main Street
Bogota, NJ 07603
Phone: 201-487-2323
Hours: Tues-Sat 11:30-6
  Sun for birthday parties only
Owner: Judith Edelstein
Specialty: Beautiful beads
Exhibiting at International Kids Show, Javits Center, New York

Payment: Cks-MC-Visa-AE
Retail: Yes
Wholesale: Bead kits only
Classes: Call for schedule
Restringing: $20 hour

Let your imagination run wild through this comfortable shop brimming with beautiful beads to suit every taste. A terrific selection including glass, ceramic, crystal, metal, plated, and vintage. The beads run the gamut from inexpensive fun stuff for children to unique finds for the serious beader. In addition you'll find a large selection of findings, ear wire, leather cord, pin backs, Fimo, Sculpey and enamel paints.
Discount coupon in back of the Directory.

BEADS GLORIOUS!
75 Prospect Terrace
Tenafly, NJ 07670
Phone/FAX: 201-568-2151
Hours: By appointment only
Owner: Anne C. S. Philipps
Exhibiting at Bead Society of Greater Washington bead bazaars.

Payment: Cks-MC-Visa-AE
Retail: Yes
Classes: By appointment
Restringing: Call for quote
Custom Work: Call for quote

A small retail business selling Japanese and Czech beads and some semiprecious beads. Anne sells at the bead society bazaars, teaches bead weaving techniques and is a lampworker and makes beads for sale. She also sells her jewelry and does jewelry repair.

RIVERSTONE
6 Hilltop Road
Medham, NJ 07945
201-543-9010
Hours: Tues-Sat 11 - 5
Owner: Rita Fennelly
Specialty: Seed bead work

Payment: Cks-MC-Visa
Retail: Yes
Classes: Call for schedule
Restringing: Yes
Custom Work: Yes
Finished Pieces: Yes

Riverstone sells ethnic jewelry, Native American arts and crafts, leather cord and findings. All kinds of beads - glass, handblown, clay, ceramic, base metal, wood and semi-precious.

THE SOJOURNER

26 Bridge Street
Lambertville, NJ 08530
Phone/FAX: 609-397-8849
Hours: Mon-Thurs 11-6
  Fri-Sat 11-9 Sun 11-6
Owner: Amy and Elsie Coss
Exhibiting at: Greater Washington area bead society bead bazaars.

Payment: Cks-MC-Visa-Disc.
Retail: Yes
Wholesale: $25 minimum

A wide variety of art, jewelry and clothing from around the world.
Also a large selection of drums and percussion instruments from
Africa, India and Indonesia. Lots of Czech glass bead, Indian glass,
metal, Balinese silver, castings, findings, and Guatemalan clay beads.

NEW MEXICO

ALL STRUNG OUT

724 N. Pueblo
PO Box 2937
Taos, NM 87571
Phone: 505-758-1235
FAX: 505-758-0014
Hours: Mon-Sat 9-5
Owner: Marcine Hughes
Specialty: Southwest, white hearts, turquoise

Payment: Cks-MC-Visa-AE
Retail: Yes
Wholesale: $100 minimum
Mail Order: Yes
Classes: Call for information

In business for seven years as a jewelry manufacturer, in 1991 they
opened their doors to the public due to the need in the area for a bead
store. Customers can come in and make their own jewelry right there.

ANAHITA GALLERY

P. O. Box 5827
Santa Fe, NM 87502
Phone: 505-820-2323
FAX: 505-820-1414
Hours: Call
Owners: Andy Hale and Kate FitzGibbon
Specialty: Ancient tribal art of Afghanistan and Pakistan
Exhibiting at: Los Angeles and San Francisco gift shows, Tucson gem
show and Santa Fe Bead Bazaar, June 1995, call for schedule.

Payment: Cks-MC-Visa-AE
Retail: Yes
Wholesale: $100 minimum
Mail Order: $100 minimum

Direct importers of authentic tribal art of Afghanistan and Pakistan.
Beads, jewelry, textiles, decorative objects, tribal silver, white metal,
brass, ancient stone and glass, ceramics, and textiles. Wholesale sales at
gift shows and consultation by appoinment.

THE BEAD CARAVAN
1801 Christine N.E.
Albuquerque, NM 87112
Phone: 505-293-7857
FAX: 505-293-9753
Hours: By appointment
Owners: Brian Curran, Robert Gilmore and Benson Lanford
Exhibiting at: Call for current schedule.

Payment: Cks-Cash
Retail: Yes
Wholesale: $300 minimum
Mail Order: Yes

A large inventory of antique and contemporary beads, ethnic jewelry and beaded objects including unusual, rare and unique beads from around the world. Inventory includes Native American section offering historic and contemporary beadwork. Art appraisal and lecture services available.

BEAD WORLD, INC.
4931 Prospect Avenue N.E.
Albuquerque, NM 87110
Phone: 505- 884-3133
FAX: 505-884-7712
Hours: Mon-Fri 9:30-6 Sat 10-4
Owner: Tom and Dan Martinez
Specialty: Indian craft supplies

Payment: Local Cks-MC-Visa
Retail: Yes
Wholesale: Yes
Mail Order: Yes
Catalog: $2 refundable
Restringing: Call for quote
Custom Work: Yes

For over 20 years this friendly bead store has been selling a large selection of all types of beads including bugle, seed, ethnic, antique, semiprecious and metal beads. A complete line of findings, watch faces, tools and supplies.

BEAUTY AND THE BEADS
418 Cerrillos Road #22
Santa Fe, NM 87501
Phone: 505-982-5234
Hours: 7 days 10-6, call for
winter hours
Owners: Madeleine and Bart Durham
Specialty: Wonderful beads

Payment: Cks-MC-Visa-AE
Retail: Yes
Wholesale: $100 minimum
Mail Order: Yes
Catalog: $3
Restringing: Yes

An unusual bead store just six blocks from the historic Plaza in downtown Santa Fe. They have many artist made beads, horn and bone, great findings and many other unusual and hard to find items. The bead shop is combined with an antiquarian bookstore to provide an interest for everyone.

CRAFT ENTERPRISES

810 W. Picacho (Hwy 70)
Las Cruces, NM 88005
Phone/FAX: 505-527-1470
Hours: Mon-Sat 9-5 Sun by appointment
Specialty: Finding unusual sources of beads
Owner: Carl Erwin

Payment: Cks-Visa-MC-Disc.
Retail: Yes
Wholesale: $100 minimum

An eclectic bead store where every bead buyer is welcome whether they are buying plastic or semi precious. A large assortment of findings by the piece or in bulk, also some craft items. The store is over 2,000 square feet of beads and supplies. Their doors are always open to bead gypsies because "you can't ever have too many beads".

INDIAN JEWELERS SUPPLY CO.

601 E. Coal Ave.
P.O. Box 1774
Gallup, NM 87305-1774
Phone: 505-722-4451
FAX: 505-722-4172
Hours: Mon-Fri 8:30 6 Sat 9-6
Owner: Employee owned

Payment: Cks-Visa-MC
Retail: Yes
Wholesale: Yes
Mail Order: $30 minimum
Catalog: $6

Southwest style metal beads, stone beads, drilled carvings and necklace kits. A comprehensive line of basic jewelers supplies and special orders for special needs. Tool for metalsmiths and lapidarits.

MAX HAND LEATHER GOODS

P. O. Box 677
Taos, NM 87571-0677
Phone: 505-758-7476
Hours: Mon-Sat 8-5
Owner: Dorothy J. Hand
Contact: Max Hand

Payment: Cks-MC-Visa
Wholesale: Yes
Mail Order: Yes
Catalog: Yes

Hand-cut deerskin thong/lacing in over 60 colors. The colors are vat-dyed into and through the leather, not painted on or surface dyed. The thong is soft, supple and very strong. It is particularly suited for stringing beads, braiding, wrapping, twisting, fringing, weaving, stitching, etc. The thong is offered in 12-foot tagged bundles for easy resale and also in 50 and 100-foot cords for cutting to specific lengths. Also pig suede in over 50 colors and a selection of unusual tools and supplies including Bond-All Clear Glue with precision applicator.

MELANIE COLLECTION

12105 Bermuda NE
Albuquerque, NM 87111
Phone/FAX: 505-298-7036
Hours: Mon-Tues-Wed 10-5
   or by appointment
Owner: Melanie Alter
Specialty: Bronze and sterling charms
Finished Pieces: Yes
Exhibiting at: Santa Fe Bead Bazaar, June 1995

Payment: Cks-MC-Visa
Retail: Yes
Wholesale: Yes pieces
Mail Order: $50 minimum
Catalog of Charms: $6
Catalog of Buttons: $2
Classes: Call for schedule

An outstanding collection of unusual things, old silver, jade, glass, handmade beads, etc. Plus an ever growing selection of reproductions of the old ethnic pieces in silver and bronze. Not too much ordinary. They also manufacture bronze and sterling charms, clasps and buttons.

111 New Mexico

MYTHMAKERS
11416 Brussels NE
Albuquerque, NM 87111
Phone: 505-299-6108
FAX: 505-299-2238
Hours: By appointment only
Owner: Nancy J. Young
Specialty: Bronze and sterling silver components
Exhibiting at Santa Fe Bead Bazaar June 16-18, 1995, and New Mexico
Bead Society bead bazaars, call for schedule.

Payment: Cks-MC-Visa
Wholesale: Yes
Mail Order: Yes
Catalog: $3

Nancy creates bronze and sterling silver components of petroglyphs
and mythmakers and/or spirit guides and some beads to be used with
them, also bronze and silver.

NINA DESIGNS

P. O. Box 5766
Santa Fe, NM 87502
Phone: 505-982-1214, 800-336-6462
FAX: 505-986-1321
Hours: Mon-Fri 11-5
Owner: Nina Cooper
Specialty: Sterling silver beads
Exhibiting at: Tucson Gem and Mineral Show, San Mateo Gem Show
and other shows, call for current schedule.

Payment: Cks-MC-Visa
Retail: Yes
Wholesale: $100 minimum
Mail Order: $50 retail minimum
   $100 wholesale minimum
Catalog: $5

Handmade sterling silver beads, charms and components. Handmade
beads, pendants and findings from their workshop in Bali, Indonesia.
Specializing in antique and ethnic reproductions as well as original
designs. **See the color insert for photos of Nina's beads.**

SIOUX TRADING POST

1428 Cerillos Road
Santa Fe, NM 87505
Phone: 505-820-0605
   800-456-3394
FAX: 505-820-1336
Hours: Mon-Sat 9:30-5:30
Owner: Ray Hillenbrand
Specialty: Native American craft supplies

Payment: Cks-MC-Visa-AE
Retail: Yes
Wholesale: $250 minimum
Mail Order: Yes
Catalog: $2

Beads from all over the world, Czech, Italian, bugle, chevron and many
others. Also beadwork, quillwork, books, tapes, videos and jewelry.
This store also sells many Native American craft supplies and Native
American finished beadwork.

SOUTHWEST AMERICA

1506-C Wyoming Blvd., NE
Albuquerque, NM 87112
Phone: 505-299-1856
Hours: Mon-Fri 10-5 Sat 10-4
Owner: John & Patricia Crawford
Specialty: Problem solving
Contact: Pat, John or Judie
Exhibiting at: New Mexico Bead Society bazaars

Payment: Cks-MC-Visa-AE
Retail: Yes
Wholesale: Quantity discounts
Mail Order: $25 minimum
Catalog: Yes
Classes: Call for schedule
Restringing: Yes
Finished Pieces: Yes

Millions of beads in a small space. Lively sales help and suggestions to
get you started or solve your design problems. Pamphlets, books and
sample designs available, plus classes when space is available. Native
American Hopi jewelry is a specialty, often incorporating glass beads.

STONE MOUNTAIN BEAD GALLERY
STONE MOUNTAIN TRADING CO.

2937 Monte Vista, NE
Albuquerque, NM 87106
Phone/FAX: 505-260-1121
Hours: Tues-Sat 11-6
   extended holiday hours
Owner: Robert Steinberg
Specialty: Gemstone beads

Payment: Cks-MC-Visa
Retail: Yes
Wholesale: Yes
Mail Order: Yes
Classes: Call for schedule
Restringing: Yes
Custom Work: Yes
Finished Pieces: Yes
Consignment: Yes

Exhibiting at: Bead Bazaars in Santa Fe, Denver, Seattle, Albuquerque and Phoenix, call for current schedule.

Voted "Albuquerque's best bead store" in a newspaper poll. Just 1/2 block east of the University of New Mexico. The store is convenient, friendly and well stocked with thousands of different beads, pendants, findings and books. Robert travels overseas and handpicks high quality jewelry, handicrafts and beads which he wholesales through Stone Mountain Trading Co., now at this address. The store also features work by local beadmakers and designers. Largest selection of semiprecious beads in town. **Discount coupon in back of Directory.**

WINONA TRADING POST
P. O. Box 324
1827 Cerrillos Road
Santa Fe, NM   87504
Phone: 505-988-4811
Hours: Tues-Sat 11-4
Owner: Sylvia Nelms
Specialty: Native American

Payment: Cks-MC-Visa
Retail: Yes
Designer Discount: Yes w/tax #

In business over 20 years selling beads from around the world and Indian craft supplies. Low prices and friendly service, longevity speaks for itself. They will do mail order if customer has tax number and a minimum of $50 order in the US only. Some of the prices here are lower than some wholesalers. Great selections here.

WORLDLY GOODS

848 Camino Del Pueblo
Bernalillo, NM 87004
Phone/FAX: 505-867-1303
Hours: Mon-Fri 10-5
Owner: Audrey Ross
Specialty: Sterling and bronze charms and components

Payment: Checks
Retail: Yes
Wholesale: $50 minimum
Mail Order: $50 minimum
Catalog: $3

Worldly Goods developed from many years of traveling around the world collecting and buying ethnic artifacts. Known as a wholesale provider who gives the customer the very best products including unusual and original beads and components in glass and cast metals.

NEW YORK

ACCENTS BEAD SHOP

513 Elmwood Avenue
Buffalo, NY 14222
Phone/FAX: 716-884-4689
Hours: Mon-Tues 10-6 Wed 10-5
   Thurs 10-7 Fri 10-6 Sat 10-4:30 Sun 12-4
Owners: Milt and Nancy Criswell
Specialty: Semiprecious and glass beads

Payment: Cks-MC-Visa
Retail: Yes
Wholesale: Bulk pricing
Mail Order: Yes
Classes: Call for schedule

Full service retail bead store and the area's largest selection of semi precious, Czech glass, seed and bugle beads and findings. An exceptional selection of lampwork glass beads and Nepalese and Tibetan metal accent pieces. A unique shopping experience and a "can't miss" for beaders in the area. Conveniently located on Elmwood near downtown.

BEAD HOUSE, INC.

20 West 37th Street
New York, NY 10018
Phone: 212-714-1420
FAX: 212-967-5015
Hours: Mon-Fri 8-5
Contact: Laura Stein
Specialty: Plating beads

Payment: Checks
Retail: Yes
Wholesale: $50 minimum
Mail Order: Yes

Located in the bead district in Manhattan selling high fashion costume jewelry, beads, craft beads, plated beads, fancy acrylic, plastic stones, plastic shapes and much more.

BEAD STORE CAFE

116 Center
Ithaca, NY 14850
Phone: 607-277-1729
Hours: Mon-Wed 10-6
   Thurs-Fri 10-8 Sat 10-6 Sun 12-5
Owner: Marta Macbeth
Specialty: Unique beads

Payment: Cks-MC-Visa-AE
Retail: Yes
Classes: Call for schedule
Restringing: Call for quote
Finished Pieces: Yes

A new store focusing only on beads, findings and related items. Special membership deal, $20 a year entitles you to class discounts, special bulk buying and free coffee. There is a table and workspace and storage service so you can leave your project there and return to complete it at your convenience. Free design assistance always offered.

BEAD STREET, LTD.

301 East Main Street
Port Jefferson, NY 11777
Phone: 516-928-3131
FAX: 516-751-0319
Hours: Mon-Wed 10-6 Thurs-Fri 10-8 Sat 10-6 Sun 12-6
Owner: Jane McChrie-Robins
Specialty: Vintage seed beads

Payment: Cks-MC-Visa-AE
Retail: Yes
Wholesale: Discounts w/tax #
Classes: Call for schedule
Restringing: Call for quote

Large variety of antique glass beads from Germany, Austria, the Czech Republic and seed beads old and new from Japan. Bali silver, semiprecious and many other unique beads from around the world. Also findings in sterling, gold filled and base metals, including fancy earwires and centerpieces, watch findings, stringing supplies, tools and books. Also antique sequins and Mexican and African folk art.

BEADS OF PARADISE

127 East 7th Street
New York, NY 10009
Phone: 212-473-1145
FAX: 212-473-3960
Hours: Tues-Sun 12-7
Owners: Brian Kenner and Richard Meyer
Specialty: African beads, textiles and artifacts

Payment: Cks-MC-Visa-AE
Retail: Yes
Wholesale: $150 minimum
Mail Order: Yes
Finished Pieces: Yes

Their emphasis is on selling rare collector beads, loose and antique beads on strands, tribal jewelry of museum quality, their own line of earrings adapted from original African designs and artifacts which include the use of beads from African cultures. They are direct importers and travel to Africa twice a year and specialize in talismanic beads, jewelry used in traditional African cultures and handwoven cloth in cotton and wool from west and central Africa.

BEADS and COSTUME JEWELRY PARTS!

For Bead Suppliers and Manufacturers.
New styles available each season.

We are a domestic manufacturer
and importer of fine quality acrylic
and metalized beads, ear buttons,
hearts, stars, bows, drops, flowers,
beef leather, novelty shapes, and more.

High fashion and classic styles for
all jewelry and accessory trades.

WHOLESALE ONLY. CATALOG AVAILABLE.

BEAD HOUSE, INC.
20 WEST 37TH STREET
NEW YORK, NY 10018

PHONE: (212) 714-1420   FAX: (212) 967-5015

BEYOND BEADERY

54 Tinker Street
Woodstock, NY 12498
Phone: 914-679-5548
Phone: 800-840-5548
Hours: Daily 11-6
Owner: Betcey Ventrella
Specialty: Seed beads

Payment: Cks-MC-Visa-AE
Retail: Yes
Wholesale: Some bulk pricing
   available
Mail Order: Yes
Catalog: $1

Located on the main strip in the town of Woodstock and just minutes off the NY State Thruway. Thousands of styles and colors of seed beads (Czech and Japanese). Also bugle beads, 3-cuts, matte iris, and acid washed beads, and many others from around the world. Also books, needles, threads, looms, and findings.

HELBY IMPORT CO.

74 Rupert Avenue
Staten Island, NY 10314
Phone: 718-447-0008
FAX: 718-447-8627
Hours: Mon-Fri 9-5
Owner: Larry Weiss

Payment: Business Cks-MC-Visa
Wholesale: To dealers only
Mail Order: Yes

Specialty: **Sells to bead**
   stores only

A primary supplier for bead stringing supplies. **Positively no retail.** The source for tools, beading needles, silk, nylon, leather string, bead boards, glue, French wire, how to books, tiger tail, storage boxes, bead looms, Nymo thread, and much more. If you own a bead shop you will want to contact this company. The widest range of bead stringing supplies at the best possible prices. **Dealers only.**

KUMA BEADS

133 Saratoga Road #3
P. O. Box 25049 Dept. TBD
Glenville, NY 12325
Phone: 518-384-0110
FAX: 518-399-0677
Hours: Mon-Sat 11-3 Thurs 6-8
Owner: Felicia Nagamatsu
Specialty: Gemstone beads

Payment: Cks-MC-Visa
Retail: Yes
Wholesale: Yes
Mail Order: Yes
Catalog: $2
Classes: Call for schedule
Custom Work: Yes
Finished Pieces: Yes

The Capital District's premiere bead shop. Quality beads and amazing low prices. Genuine gemstone beads, amethyst, garnet, hematite, crystal, carnelian, turquoise, 14K gold and seed beads, antique glass, unusual accents and much more. Jewelry findings, tools, books and classes. Convenient location, plenty of parking on Rt. 50, between Schenectady and Saratoga Springs en route to Lake George and skiing.

MARGOLA IMPORT CORP

48 W. 37th Street
New York, NY 10018
Phone: 212-695-1115
FAX: 212-594-0071
Hours: Mon-Fri 9-4:30
Owners: Robert Kanen, Neil Chalfin
Contact: Lori Mensik
Exhibiting at: Hobby Industries of America

Payment: Business Cks-MC-Visa
Retail: Yes
Wholesale: $50 minimum
Mail Order: Yes
Catalog: Yes

Margola sells Czech glass, seed, bugle, long bugle, and 2- and 3-cut beads. Also a large variety of round, firepolish, fancy beads, acrylic and glass rhinestones and jewels.

MYRON TOBACK INC.

25 West 47th Street
New York, NY 10036
Phone: 212-398-8300
FAX: 212-869-0808
Hours: Mon-Fri 8-4
Owners: Myron and Elaine Toback
Specialty: Great selection

Payment: Cks-MC-Visa-AE
Wholesale: $20 minimum
Mail Order: $20 minimum

Complete stockroom of findings, beads, sheet wire, tools and stringing supplies. Knowledgeable sales staff, friendly service, will ship all orders within 24 hours. All sterling silver, gold filled and 14K gold beads, some original and handmade.

YORK NOVELTY IMPORT, INC.

10 W. 37th Street
New York, NY 10018
Phone: 212-594-7040, 800-223-6676
FAX: 212-594-8226
Hours: Mon-Fri 9-5
Owner: Martin Bookstein
Contact: Perry Bookstein
Specialty: Czech glass beads

Payment: Cash-Cks
Retail: In person only
Wholesale: $100 minimum
Mail Order: Yes
Catalog: Free to wholesale
  buyers only

Quantity buyers only, $100 first time minimum order. Retail only in-person New York City. Family run business, now third generation, selling Czech glass, seed, bugles, 3-cut, fire polish, lampwork beads, imitation pearls, plastic plated beads, wood beads and rare finds.

NORTH CAROLINA

BEAD STRUK

610 Glenwood Avenue
Raleigh, NC 27603
Phone: 919-833-6070
Hours: Tues-Sun 1-6:30
Owner: Sally L. Lewis
Specialty: Porcelain beads

Payment: Cks-MC-Visa-AE
Retail: Yes
Wholesale: Yes
Mail Order: Yes
Finished Pieces: Yes
Restringing: $15 per strand
Custom Work: $25 and up

The only bead store in Raleigh with two rooms, one a gallery and one full of beads. Specialty beads and Sally's handmade porcelain beads in 26 colors, glazed and unglazed. Specialty threads and shows featuring local or North Carolinan artists. Classes by local artists in bead weaving and Native American traditions. Beads from around the world.

NIGHT BEAR BEADWORKS

2919 Keever Dairy Road
Iron Station, NC 28080
Phone: 704-732-2849
Hours: By appointment only
Owner: Andrew P. Drinkwater
Specialty: Custom work in
  sizes 16°-24° beads
Exhibiting at: Southeastern powwow circuit

Payment: Checks
Retail: Yes
Mail Order: Yes
Catalog: $1
Classes: Call for schedule
Custom Work: Yes
Finished Pieces: Yes

Specializing in the hard to find colors and sizes in seed beads. Large selection of seed beads sizes 13°- 24° Many old colors available and matching service available by sending samples to be matched. A small company that tries hard to meet the customer's needs. The inventory is varied and constantly changing so it is best to call and inquire.

THE ORIGINAL ORNAMENT

145 East Franklin Street
Chapel Hill, NC 27514
Phone: 919-933-3467
FAX: 919-933-4557
Hours: Mon-Sat 10-6
Owner: Rebecca Schner-Martenis

Payment: Cks-MC-Visa
Retail: Yes
Wholesale: $50 minimum
Mail Order: Yes
Finished Pieces: Yes
Classes: Call for schedule

A full-service bead shop selling loose beads, findings, tools and books. Custom work available and repairs of almost any nature. The bulk of the business is student oriented so people are always making jewelry in the store with the assistance of the experienced staff. The upstairs gallery space provides an outlet for the beadwork of the owners and of local artists as well. A diverse selection of beads from around the world including antiques and a large selection of new Chinese silver and enamelled beads.

THE RODDY GALLERY OF WAXHAW

P. O. Box 214
111 S. Main Street
Waxhaw, NC 28173
Phone: 704-283-5192
Hours: Wed-Fri 11:30-5 Sat 10-5
   Sun 12-5 or by appointment
Owners: Frank and Mary Roddy
Specialty: Antique beads and lampworked beads
Exhibiting at: Call for current schedule.

Payment: Cks-MC-Visa-AE
Retail: Yes
Wholesale: Quantity discounts
Mail Order: Yes
Finished Pieces: Yes
Restringing: Call for quote

Located in an historic North Carolina antique village, approximately 15 miles south of Charlotte, The Gallery is a spacious bead center. Collectors, designer and novice beaders can savor the experience of exploring an inventory that has been carefully selected over many years of travel and business in Europe, Latin America and Southeast Asia. Noted for the quality of unusual beads and components, The Gallery is constantly adding new, innovative and state-of-the-art beads, supplies and equipment. Also textiles, ethnographic pieces, jewelry, antiques and contemporary folk art.

A **beading needle** is a slim wire needle made especially for beadwork. Size 10 is the largest needle and size 16 is the smallest.

THE SOURCE ROCK SHOP

900 Georgia Hwy 441 So.
Franklin, NC 28734
Phone/FAX: 704-524-6511
Hours: Mon-Sun 9-7
  Winter Mon-Sun 9-5
Owner: Sandra Frary
Specialty: Gemstone beads

Payment: Checks
Retail: Yes
Wholesale: $25 minimum
Mail Order: $10 minimum
Catalog: $3
Custom Work: Yes
Restringing: Yes
Finished Pieces: Yes

A gem and mineral store selling all types of beads, mineral specimens, some rough cutting, all types of cut stones, Indian glass, wood and pewter. Ask about occasional specials. Also fossils and custom silver and gold jewelry.

OHIO

A2Z CRAFT SUPPLY

1417 Wayne Avenue
Dayton, OH 45410
Phone: 513-222-5004
Hours: Mon-Sat 10-5
Owners: Mary Barlow and Velda Donaldson

Payment: Cks
Retail: Yes
Mail Order: $25 minimum
Finished Pieces: Yes
Consignment: Yes

A small store, well stocked for all types of crafts and items used for rendezvous and Indian powwows. They can special order items for you and sell special wood cuts done with patterns of names, animals, etc. Jewelry findings and seasonal products for all the holidays.

BEADS & THINGS

8 N. Shafer Street
Athens, OH 45701
Phone: 614-592-6453
Hours: Mon-Sat 10-6
Owner: Jo E. Merkle and Phil Berry

Payment: Cks-Cash
Retail: Yes
Mail Order: Yes

A small, retail bead store with a wide variety of beads from around the world. No formal classes but anyone that comes in and wants to learn, they will gladly show the basics of using headpins, picking threads and other bead tips. For more advanced projects, there are many how-to books and always a 20% discount to anyone with a valid resale number. Also threads, needles, looms, findings.

BEAD PARADISE

15-1/2 West College Street
Oberlin, OH 44074
Phone: 216-775-2233
Hours: Mon-Sat 10-6
Owner: Ruth
Specialty: African trade beads

Payment: Cks-MC-Visa
Retail: Yes
Wholesale: African trade beads
  $100 minimum
Classes: Call for schedule

Vintage glass beads, African trade beads, semiprecious beads and carvings, seed and bugle beads, looms, stringing supplies and a complete selection of findings, as well as ancient and modern art objects.

BYZANTIUM

245 King Avenue
Columbus, OH 43201
Phone: 614-291-3130
Hours: Mon-Sat 12-7 Sun 12-6
Owner: Joyce Griffiths
Specialty: Ethnic beads

Payment: Cks-MC-Visa-AE
Retail: Yes
Designer Discount: Inquire
Mail Order: Yes, limited
Classes: Call for schedule
Finished Pieces: Yes

As capital of the Byzantine empire, the original Byzantium was a center for trade in the ancient world, presenting wonderful items from all parts of the globe. So it is with the modern Byzantium, offering a huge selection of beads, many of them vintage, antique and ancient. Also available a large variety of books, findings, finished jewelry by their talented staff, ethnic jewelry and art, and sterling silver jewelry. The staff is available for bead technique consultation. All in a beautiful setting. Plan to spend some time exploring this great store and the Byzantium Bead Museum and Library. Worth the trip to Ohio!

DISCOUNT BEAD HOUSE

P. O. Box 186, The Plains OH 45780
60 N. Court Street
Athens, OH 45701
Phone: 614-593-3587, 800-793-7592
Hours: Mon-Sat 10:30-5 Sun 12-4
Owners: Marty and Andrea Stern
Specialty: Seed beads
Exhibiting at: Central Ohio Bead Society sale, call for current schedule.

Payment: Cks
Retail: Yes
Mail Order: Yes
Catalog: Free if you mention
  The Bead Directory
Finished Pieces: Yes

Why pay retail or buy more than you need? Seed beads, Czech, *delicas*, antiques and hex beads. Join the Bead Club and never miss a new color. Up to 12 colors sent monthly in any of the three types listed all at below retail. Also all related beading supplies, needles, findings, Fimo and Cernit. Small orders accepted.

GRANGER CITY ANTIQUES & BEADS
17923 Detroit Avenue   **Payment**: Cks
Lakewood, OH 44107   **Retail**: Yes
Phone: 216-521-1617   **Mail Order**: Yes
  800-793-7592
Hours: Wed, Fri-Sat 12:30-5 Sun 12:30-4
Owner: Phyllis Basen
Specialty: Antique beads

All kinds of beads and antiques and collectibles. Create your own or they will assist you. Got beads to sell; call Phyllis, she buys beads.

ISLE OF BEADS
2483 Lee Boulevard   **Payment**: Local Cks-MC-Visa
Cleveland Heights, OH 44118   **Retail**: Yes
Phone: 216-371-0173   **Classes**: Call for schedule
Hours: Tues-Sat Noon-6   **Finished Pieces**: Yes
Owner: Denise Newman   **Consignment**: Call for details
Specialty: European beads   **Gallery**: Call for details

The Isle of Beads arose from the Sea of No Bead in summer of 1991, immediately attracting mermaids and bead people from near and far. This many faceted Queendom has kilos of beads to bugle about. Nomadic traders and UPS men bring exciting beads to the island's shore. The Queen and her court teach many visitors about the lore and workings of beads, including glass beadmaking. The beach is located just north of where Lee flows over Mayfield in Cleveland Heights. You'll also find finished beaded artwork, books and findings at the Isle.

OKLAHOMA

INTERNATIONAL BEADTRADER
3323 R East 51st Street   **Payment**: Cks-MC-Visa
Tulsa, OK 74135   **Retail**: Yes
Phone: 918-743-3405   **Mail Order**: Yes
Hours: Call   **Catalog**: $5 refundable
Owner: Jim Brock   **Classes**: Call for schedule
Specialty: Wide selection   **Restringing**: Call for quote

A direct importer of a tremendous selection of beads from around the world. A wide variety of beads, findings and supplies.

INTERNATIONAL BEADTRADER

735 Asp Avenue
Norman, OK 73069
Phone: 405-321-7722
Hours: Call
Owner: Jim Brock
Specialty: Wide selection

Payment: Cks-MC-Visa
Retail: Yes
Mail Order: Yes
Catalog: $5 refundable
Classes: Call for schedule
Restringing: Call for quote

A direct importer of a tremendous selection of beads from around the world. A wide variety of beads, findings and supplies.

OREGON

Adornments

A Unique Bead & Jewelry Gallery

209 West Main Street ❋ Medford, Oregon 97501
503 - 772-2309

❋ Vintage Beads   ❋ Findings
❋ One of a kind Pieces   ❋ Tools
❋ Custom Designing   ❋ Consignment Pieces

Business Hours:
10 a.m. to 5:30 p.m. - Tuesday through Friday
10 a.m. to 5 p.m. - Saturday

A Store for the Distinctive Personality

ADORNMENTS

209 West Main Street
Medford, OR 97501
Phone: 503-772-2309
Hours: Mon-Sat
Owner: Diane Robins
Specialty: Unique designs

Payment: Cks-MC-Visa-AE
Retail: Yes
Designer Discount: Ask for info.
Mail Order: Yes
Classes: Call for schedule

A great selection of beads from around the world. You'll find a lot of unique and unusual beads here and also findings, books and Diane's own custom designs.

AFRICA JOHN'S

P. O. Box 565
Blodgett, OR 97326
Phone: 503-456-2012
FAX: 503-456-2046
Owner: John R. Paulas
Specialty: One-of-a-kind

Payment: Cash-Cks
Retail: Yes
Wholesale: Yes
Mail Order: Yes
Custom Work: Yes
Finished Pieces: Yes

John produces Saharan-style beads of ancient and antique form. Custom beads made to order cut directly from the finest raw minerals and organic materials. Also North African Amazonite, amber, coral, agate, quartz, silver, opal, ebony and lapis.

BAKER BAY BEAD CO.

35655 Shoreview Drive
Dorena, OR 97434
Phone: 503-942-3941
FAX: 503-942-8479 (24 hrs)
Hours: Mail order - Mon-Fri 8-5
  Showroom by appointment only
Owners: Bud and Cecelia Heykamp
Specialty: Good selection, good service
Exhibiting at: Many powwows and Black Powder/Mountain Man shows in Washington, Oregon and California. Call for schedule.

Payment: Cks
Retail: Yes
Wholesale: Yes
Mail Order: Yes
Catalog: $2

Excellent quality glass beads in a large variety of styles, sizes and colors. Seed beads in sizes from 6° - 15° , cut beads 9° - 15° including Charlotte and hex cuts, bugles, crow, faceted and many unique shapes. Mostly Czech but also Japanese 15° in seed and hex and 11° seed. Also shell, abalone, metal beads and findings, beading supplies, instruction books, looms and other accessories necessary for beadwork. A vast selection of authentic old trade beads for sale but no catalog at this time. Wholesale mail order catalog available for all other beads and fast service, same day for normal orders. The impossible orders take 24 hours. **Coupon for $2 off 1st order with mention of The Bead Directory.**

Round nose pliers are used for making loops and twisting and bending circles. **Flat nose pliers** are used for crimping. **Needle nose pliers** are used for holding or gripping and for breaking off damaged beads.

THE BEAD GARDEN

1313 Mill Street, S.E.
Salem, OR 97301
Phone: 503-391-9285
Hours: Tues-Sat 10-4:30
Owner: Lorie Bickford
Specialty: Czech and lampworked glass

Payment: Local Cks-MC-Visa
Retail: Yes
Classes: Call for schedule
Restringing: $10 per hour
Finished Pieces: Yes

The Bead Garden is a specialty shop offering quality beads, findings, books, supplies and classes for the serious and not so serious beadworker. Loose and strung beads, manufactured from a variety of different materials and coming from around the world, give crafters and collectors a wide selection from which to choose. Also featured is jewelry and other beadwork from local craftspeople. The atmosphere of the shop is such that customers are encouraged to take their time in choosing the raw materials for their bead creations. Help and advice are always available if needed and cheerfully given when requested. Consignment beadwork, over 80 book titles, thread, and Fimo.

THE BEAD MERCHANT

300 S.W. 6th Street
Grants Pass, OR 97526
Phone/FAX: 503-471-0645
Hours: Mon-Fri 10-5:30 Sat 10-5
Owner: Julee and Bruce Parsons
Specialty: Czech beads

Payment: Cks-MC-Visa
Retail: Yes
Wholesale: $50 minimum
Mail Order: $25 minimum
Catalog: Yes
Classes: Call for schedule
Restringing: Call for quote
Custom Work: Yes

When you enter The Bead Merchant, you enter a whole new world. Surrounded by pleasant music, ethnic art, gifts, fabrics and baskets, you can enjoy table after table of beads from around the world. Displayed on open tables, by color, making it easy to choose the beads you want. The beads are sold loose, by the strand or in bulk packages. Findings of all varieties are also sold in bulk packages. Also beading cord, leather thong, ethnic clothing and fabrics, watch parts, books and local art. The gallery features a different artist each month. Call for information on having your beadwork displayed.

A matte bead is a glass bead with a dull, low-luster surface produced by etching in an acid bath or by tumbling.

A BEAD SOURCE

15831 S.E. Division
Portland, OR 97236
Phone/FAX: 503-760-8964
Hours: Mon-Sat 10-5:30
Owner: Dixie Thompson
Exhibiting at: Portland Bead Society bazaar.

Payment: Local Cks-MC-Visa
Retail: Yes
Wholesale: $100 minimum
Finished Pieces: Yes

All kinds of semiprecious and glass, both Czech and Japanese seed beads in sizes 8°-15°, beads from around the world and everything you need to make great bead creations.

BEAD STREET

632 NW 21st Avenue
Portland, OR 97209
Phone/FAX: 503-223-7728
Hours: Mon-Fri 11-7 Sat 11-6
  Sun 12-6
Owners: Patsy and Colleen Compton
Specialty: African trade and Czech beads
Exhibiting at: Portland Bead Society bazaar and other shows, call for current schedule

Payment: Cks-MC-Visa
Retail: Yes
Mail Order: $25 minimum
Classes: Call for schedule
Restringing: $1.50 per inch
Custom Work: Call for quote

Beads from around the world. Many of the beads are one of a kind and/or special pieces hand carried from far away places. The large inventory offers you the widest variety and selection of beads. They rotate the inventory frequently to offer new and exciting merchandise every time you visit. Don't know where to begin? The staff will help. Look at the samples, take a class, select a book from the large inventory. A large selection of charms and leather thong.

THE BEAD STUDIO

14 South First Street
Ashland, OR 97520
Phone/FAX: 503-488-3037
1-800-25 BEADS (252-3237)
Hours: Mon-Sat 10:30-6 Sun 12-5
Owner: Pamela Landell
Specialty: Great selection

Payment: Cks-MC-Visa-Disc.
Retail: Yes
Wholesale: $20 minimum
Mail Order: $25 minimum
Catalog: Free
Classes: Call for schedule
Restringing: Call for quote
Custom Work: Call for quote

A full service bead store taking pride in displaying the abundant selection of beads in a way that makes the beads easily accessible so you can touch, feel and compare. The owner is a jewelry designer whose love of beads and appreciation of the art shows in the selection that is offered at the store. Also charms, books, tools and findings and supplies.

C&GG (CRAFTS & GIFTS GALORE)

633 Main Street
Klamath Falls, OR 97601
Phone/FAX: 503-884-9973
  1-800-601-9974
Hours: Mon-Sat 10-5
Owner: Marge Lawson
Specialty: Charms

Payment: Cks-MC-Visa
Retail: Yes
Wholesale: $50 minimum
Mail Order: $50 minimum
Catalog: Free
Restringing: Call for quote

The retail store has a combination of gifts, craft supplies, beads and findings. The mail order catalog has tools, equipment, stringing materials, base metal charms, base metal findings, sterling silver charms and chains, sterling silver and gold filled findings and beads.

DAVA BEAD & TRADE

6357 SW Capitol Hwy
Portland, OR 97201
Phone: 503-246-1934
Hours: Mon-Wed & Fri 10-6
      Thurs 10-8 Sat 10-5
Owner: Anita Bermont
Finished Pieces: Yes
Exhibiting at: Portland Bead Society Bazaar, November.

Payment: Cks-MC-Visa
Retail: Yes
Wholesale: Quantity discounts
Mail Order: Yes
Classes: Call for schedule
Restringing: Yes
Custom Work: Yes

Dava Bead and Trade offers an international selection of beads, components and findings. Their seasonal workshops provide an inspiring environment for the study of beadwork and its related applications.

DEON'S DESIGNS ORIGINALE

P. O. Box 125
265 Highway 101
Waldport, OR 97394
Phone/FAX: 503-563-5300
Hours: Mon-Sun 10-5
Owner: Deon DeLange
Specialty: Beadwork books

Payment: Cks
Retail: Yes
Classes: Yes, call
Restringing: Call for quote
Custom Work: Yes
Consignment: Yes
Gallery: Yes

Retail supplier for seed and bugle beads, larger accent beads (glass, metal, etc.) books, classes, findings, etc. Deon will gladly autograph any of her books or videos: *Techniques of Beaded Earrings*, ($7.95 book, $29.95 video), *More Techniques of Beading Earrings*, ($8.95). Contact her to schedule a showing of your unusual or one-of-a-kind beadwork. The store is located on the beautiful Oregon coast. Also available are copper enamelled beads made by Deon's husband Don.

FIRE MOUNTAIN GEMS

28195 Redwood Highway
Cave Junction, OR 97523
Phone: 800-423-2319
FAX: 503-592-3103
Hours: Mon-Fri 7-5
Owners Chris and Stuart Freedman
Specialty: Latest trends

Payment: Cks-MC-Visa-AE
Wholesale: Yes
Mail Order: Yes
Catalog: $3

Over 20,000 jewelry and craft components. This includes a huge selection of beads and stringing supplies, gemstones and mountings, adhesives, feathers, etc. Everything to manufacture jewelry yourself. Wholesale to the trade.

HARLEQUIN BEADS

1091 Olive Street
Eugene, OR 97401
Phone: 503-683-5903 or
   800-234-2359
Hours: Mon-Sat 10-6 Sun 12-5
Owner: Stacy Bierma

Payment: Cks
Retail: Yes
Wholesale: Quantity discounts
Mail Order: Yes
Catalog: $1
Restringing: Call for quote
Custom Work: Call for quote
Finished Pieces: Yes

Large selection of rare and antique beads from around the world available by the bead or in bulk. Lots of Czech seed beads and crystal, Austrian crystal beads and prisms, antique German glass, African trade beads, findings, books and finished jewelry.

LOOKING GLASS BEADS

283 E. Main Street
Ashland, OR 97520
Phone: 503-482-7000, 800-736-4232
FAX: 503-482-7700
Hours: Mon-Sat 10:30 - 5:30
Owner: Mary Moore
Specialty: Unique beads

Payment: Cks-MC-Visa
Retail: Yes
Wholesale: $20 minimum
Mail Order: $25 minimum
Catalog: $5
Classes: Call for schedule
Restringing: Call for quote

Exhibiting at: Oregon Country Fair, July 7-9, Booth #878.

You'll find antique cases filled with old and new beads from around the world at this bead store. Also all the basic beading supplies including threads, findings and tools. A large selection of seed beads and imported glass beads from India. The owner travels the world to find unique beads for the store.

MULTNOMAH BEAD GALLERY

7872 SW Capitol Highway
Portland, OR 97219
Phone/FAX: 503-245-7667
Hours: Mon-Wed 11-6
  Thurs-Fri 11-7 Sat 11-6 Sun 12-5
Owner: Terry Compton
Specialty: Ethnic beads

Payment: Cks-MC-Visa
Retail: Yes
Classes: Call for schedule
Restringing: Call for quote

Exhibiting at: Portland Bead Society bazaar

Located in charming Multnomah Village known to Oregonians for its art center, antique row and fine restaurants. In addition to the extensive collection of beads, findings, tools and books, the Gallery also offers hands on creative help to facilitate beginners and professionals' efforts. A discount club is open to all customers and offers a bead referral service. Free childrens classes twice a week.

OUT OF THE BLUE

P. O. Box 834
Ashland, OR 97520
Phone: 503-488-2191
Hours: By appointment
Owner: Kathleen Kuzmitz
Specialty: Quality selection

Payment: Cks
Retail: Yes
Wholesale: Quantity discounts
Mail Order: Yes

Exhibiting at: Many bazaars, call for dates and locations

An extensive inventory of high quality contemporary, vintage, ethnic, metal and semiprecious stone beads and unique components, plus a complete selection of findings, tools, and books as well as unique adornments.

PORTLAND BEAD COMPANY

800 SW Alder Street
Portland, OR 97205
Phone/FAX: 503-243-2543
Hours: Mon-Sat 11-6 Sun 12-5
  Thurs-Fri 11-7 Sat 11-6 Sun 12-5
Owner: Theresa Compton
Specialty: Antique beads
Exhibiting at: Portland Bead Society bazaar

Payment: Cks-MC-Visa
Retail: Yes
Classes: Call for schedule
Finished Pieces: Yes

Since 1988 this store has expanded to over 1,700 square feet and houses a great selection of the most unique and sought after beads. The owner's interest in beads, beaded antique clothing and antiques has led her on many a journey to find one-of-a-kind pieces to bring back to her store. Lots of Czech and Japanese seed beads, antiques and curios.

RAINBOW BEAD CO.

P. O. Box 82566
Portland, OR 97282-0566
Phone/FAX: 503-774-1401
Hours: By appointment only
Owner: Fran and Murray Stone
Specialty: Japanese seed beads
Exhibiting at: 3rd International Bead Conference, Washington, D.C., November 1995

Payment: Cks-C.O.D.
Wholesale: Yes
Mail Order: Yes
Catalog: Yes

Direct importer of Japanese seed beads. "Toho" Japanese seed beads, antique, 11° and 15° round, 15° hex, 8° round, hex, bugles and Magatama.

SOUTHWEST TRADING POST

234 Liberty N.E.
Salem, OR 97301
Phone: 503-364-4668
Hours: Mon-Sat 10-6 Sun 12-5
Owner: Donna Yutzy
Specialty: Native American

Payment: Local Cks-MC-Visa
Retail: Yes
Restringing: Call for quote

This store has a Southwest focus carrying fine handcrafted Native American items. Silver jewelry, pottery, Kachinas, rugs and much more. Also a good selection of crystals and crystal jewelry. The family imports Brazilian agates and a large selection of other stones. The bead selection is large and diverse with seed beads in many colors and sizes, and beads of glass, metal, clay, etc. and a large selection of findings, books and beading supplies.

TIERRACAST

Box 241
Aurora, OR 97002
Phone: 503-678-2926
FAX: 503-678-2927
Hours: By appointment only
Sales Rep: Pam Arion
Specialty: Unique findings

Payment: Cks-C.O.D.
Wholesale: $100 minimum
Mail Order: $100 minimum
Catalog: Free

Wholesale only, no retail calls. Supplying bead stores with high quality, innovative designed castings to plan your beads around including silver, gold and copper plated pewter. Earring, bracelet and necklace pieces, toggle clasps, charms, posts, ear clips and pendants. Also custom earwire and earhoops in sterling, gold filled, 14K and niobium. Ask your local bead store to order for you.

WORLDBEADS

2320 NW Westover Road
Portland, OR 97210
Phone: 503-228-8820
Hours: Call

Payment: Cks-MC-Visa
Retail: Yes
Mail Order: Yes
Classes: Call for schedule
Custom Work: Yes

Create your own accessories shop. Large selection of quality beads, findings, leather, books and more.

PENNSYLVANIA

COCHRAN'S CRAFTS
845 Willow Road
Lancaster, PA 17601
Phone: 717-392-1865
Hours: By appointment
Owner: Bill and Betty Cochran
Specialty: Plated beads

Payment: Cks
Retail: Yes
Wholesale: Yes
Mail Order: Yes
Catalog: SASE

Brass and nickel plated beads, plain round and fluted, antique trade, Czech, Japanese, French seed and bugle beads. Books on bead research.

BARBARA ANN VOLK DESIGNS
41 Baltimore Street
Glen Rock, PA 17327
Phone: 717-235-3868
Hours: By appointment only
Owner: Barbara Ann Volk
Specialty: Setting stones w/beads
Finished Pieces: Yes
Exhibiting at: Call or write for current schedule

Payment: Cks
Retail: Yes
Wholesale: $250 minimum
Mail Order: Yes
Price/Product List: $1
Classes: Call for schedule
Custom Work: Yes

Heart-felt wearable art using seed beads and precious and semiprecious gemstones. Author of a workbook for beadworkers on stone setting techniques; *Setting Stones with Beads*.

SOUTH CAROLINA

ONE BY ONE
315 Augusta Street
Greenville, SC 29601
Phone: 803-421-0113
   1-800-449-3658
FAX: 803-421-0312
Hours: Mon-Thurs 2-6 Fri-Sat 10-6
   Sunday by appointment
Owners: Mark Hardies and Diane Prekup
Specialty: Czech beads

Payment: Cks-MC-Visa
Retail: Yes
Mail Order: Yes
Classes: Call for schedule
Finished Pieces: Yes
Restringing: Call for quote
Custom Work: Yes

A unique blend of ethnic, classic, unusual and colorful beads. The only store of its kind in the area offering classes in beaded jewelry and bead weaving by experienced designers. Beads are added to the collection from all over the world on a regular basis. Custom jewery design available and also findings, tools and thread.

RED PIANO TOO ART GALLERY

P. O. Box 993
853 Sea Island Pkwy (Hwy 21)
St. Helena Island, SC 29920
Phone: 803-838-2241
FAX: 803-838-5638
Hours: By appointment only
Owner: Elayne T. Scott

Payment: Cks-C.O.D.
Wholesale: $100 minimum
Mail Order: $30 minimum

Specialty: Southeastern artists

Located on St. Helena Island The Gallery is 12 colorful, rambling rooms. The collection includes artwork by many well-known Southeastern artists and an extensive selection of ethnic beads from around the world. The other rooms feature African art, unique prints and the Pat Conroy book room.

SOUTH DAKOTA

SIOUX TRADING POST

415 6th Street
Rapid City, SD 57701
Phone: 605-348-4822
Orders: 1-800-456-3394
Hours: Call
Owner: Ray Hillenbrand
Specialty: Italian glass beads

Payment: Cks-MC-Visa-AE
Retail: Yes
Wholesale: $200 craft supplies
Mail Order: Yes
Catalog: Yes
Classes: Call
Finished Pieces: Yes
Gallery Space: Yes

This is a working trading post at the edge of the Black Hills of South Dakota, not far from the reservations at Pine Ridge, Rosebud and Cheyenne River. They sell all kinds of old and new beads. They provide the highest quality craft supplies for local and mail-order craft workers and buy finished goods from Native Americans only (must be tribally registered as they are IACA certified). Plains Indian-made beadwork, quillwork and silver jewelry. Two locations, one in Rapid City and the other in Mission on the Rosebud Reservation.

> **TIP**: "Many people, because they feel inhibited by the idea of "designing", consider it a problem and avoid it. The truth is, it really is quite fun if you don't get too serious about it. Don't worry if you think you can't draw, or that your drawings look rough. Just have fun and play. You'll be surprised how quickly you get the hang of designing when you see it as fun." *Setting Stones With Beads*, Barbara Ann Volk.

TENNESSEE

LAND OF ODDS
174 Second Avenue North
Nashville, TN 37201
Phone: 615-254-4341
Hours: Mon-Wed 10-6 Thurs 10-9
 Fri-Sat 10-11 Sun 12-5
Owners: Warren Feld and
 James Jones
Specialty: Glass beads

Payment: Cks-MC-Visa-AE
Retail: Yes
Wholesale: $100 minimum
Mail Order: $50 minimum
Catalog: Yes
Restringing: Call for quote
Finished Pieces: Yes
Consignment: Call for details

Jewelry studio and bead shop selling custom designed jewelry, extraordinary gifts and collectibles. Nashville's largest bead and finding store specializing in glass and semi precious stone beads. The owners work with silver, bronze, copper and stones to create unique jewelry and objects d'art.

TEXAS

ALEXANDER-LEE
P. O. Box 37042
Houston, TX 77237-7042
Phone/FAX: 713-789-2564
Hours: Mon-Fri 10-6
Owners: Susan and Phillip Holland
Specialty: Venetian beads
Exhibiting at: Many shows, call for current schedule

Payment: Cks-MC-Visa-AE
Retail: Yes
Wholesale: $100 minimum
Mail Order: $100 minimum
Catalog: By written request $5
Finished Pieces: Yes

Since 1976 selling only Venetian beads. Direct importers carrying over 200 styles and colors of loose beads. Also necklaces, earrings, bracelets and pendants.

BALLY BEAD COMPANY
2304 Ridge Road
Rockwall, TX 75087
Phone: 214-771-4515
FAX: 214-722-1979
Hours: Mon-Fri 9-5 Sat 9-1
Owner: Ward Hudspeth

Payment: Cks-MC-Visa-Disc.
Wholesale: Yes
Mail Order: $50 minimum
Catalog: $5

Showroom and warehouse just minutes from downtown Dallas, Importer, manufacturer and distributor of great beads.

BEAD IT!

750 Sunland Park Drive
Sunland Park Mall
El Paso, TX 79912
Phone: 915-587-5512
Hours: Mon-Sat 10-9 Sun 12-6
Owners: Alessandra Scamardo
Specialty: Czech beads

Payment: Cks-MC-Visa
Retail: Yes
Mail Order: $25 minimum
Catalog: Yes
Classes: Yes, call
Finished Pieces: Yes

Located in beautiful Sunland Park Mall in West El Paso. One of the largest selections of Czech and Japanese seed beads in the area. A great selection of unusual beads and components from around the world, findings, tools, supplies and lots of books. The staff is happy to assist you with design questions. Lots of contemporary lampworked beads by nationally known artists.

CELEBRATION!

108 W. 43rd Street
Austin, TX 78751
Phone: 512-453-6207
FAX: 512-453-6207
Hours: Mon-Sat 10-6:30 Sun 12:30 - 5
Owners: Shirley Danforth, Winifred Simon
Specialty: Vintage Bohemian

Payment: Cks-MC-Visa-AE
Retail: Yes

Make your own treasure necklace with Goddess pendants or any of the other spiritual accent pieces. The knowledgeable staff can assist with beads, accent pieces, and other selections in a peaceful, unhurried atmosphere. They sell vintage Bohemian, African trade, seed, Indian natural stone, metal, Peruvian, Japanese, Chinese and many other odd and unusual beads from around the world.

LAS CANADAS TRADING CO. (THE BEAD SHOP)

2435 Interstate 40 West
Amarillo, TX 79109
Phone: 806-358-0562
Hours: Mon-Fri 10-6 Sat 10-5
Owners: Jim McGee & C.P. Miller
Specialty: Seed beads

Payment: Cks-MC-Visa
Retail: Yes
Mail Order: $25 minimum
Restringing: Call for quote
Finished Pieces: Yes
Classes: Yes, call

Retail sales of four sizes of seed beads from the Czech Republic and Japan. Also trade beads, semiprecious stone beads and chips. Native craft supplies and all findings and supplies needed for all forms of beadwork. Southwest silver and turquoise jewelry gift items for sale and on consignment terms.

MILA'S BOUTIQUE

1507 W. Koenig Lane
Austin, TX 78756
Phone: 512-452-3190
Hours: Tues-Sat 11-4
  or by appointment
Owner: Mila Crowell
Specialty: Czech rocailles and bugle beads

Payment: Cks-MC-Visa
Wholesale: Kilo minimum
Retail: Yes
Mail Order: $25 minimum
Finished Pieces: Yes
Classes: Call for schedule

A wide range of supplies for the do-it-yourself costumer and beader including beads, trims, appliques, rhinestones, sequins, and fabric. The largest selection of silver lined rocailles and bugles in the area.

WORLDBEADS

Village Arcade
2505 Amherst
Houston, TX 77005
Phone: 713-526-8438
Hours: Call
Specialty: Unique selection

Payment: Cks-MC-Visa
Retail: Yes
Mail Order: Yes
Catalog: $10
Classes: Call for schedule

Beads from around the world, unique findings and lots of bead books.

UTAH

EAGLE FEATHER TRADING POST

168 West 12th Street
Ogden, UT 84404
Phone: 801-393-3991
FAX: 801-745-0903
Hours: Mon-Sat 9- 6
Owner: Eaglecrafts, Inc.
Contact: Sue or Chris
Specialty: Native American crafts

Payment: Cks-MC-Visa-AE
Retail: Yes
Wholesale: Yes
Mail Order: Yes
Catalog: $3

All kinds of beads, related craft supplies and lots of books. They specialize in Native American crafts and mountain man supplies.

MOABILIA

135 N. Main
Moab, UT 84532
Phone: 801-259-1601
Hours: Mon-Sun 10-10
  Call for winter hours
Owners: Solange Roussin
Specialty: Great beads

Payment: Cks-MC-Visa
Retail: Yes
Designer Discount: 10%
Finished Pieces: Yes

A great selection of old and new unusual beads and ethnic jewelry from all over the world. Silver, glass, ceramic, stone, amber and Fimo. Also featuring fine work by local and national designers and Southwestern style gifts such as pottery, baskets and rugs.

VERMONT

OPTIONAL EXTRAS

55 San Remo Drive
South Burlington, VT 05403
Phone: 802-658-0013
FAX: 802-864-5030
Hours: Mon-Sat 11-5
Specialty: Glass beads

Payment: Cks-MC-Visa-AE
Retail: Yes
Wholesale: Yes
Mail Order: Yes
Catalog: $1

Thousands of beads are on display in the hands-on warehouse showroom. A direct importer from many countries selling an overwhelming selection of beads from around the world. Spacious store with worktable to experiment and an incredible full-color mail order catalog. Located less than a mile from Interstate 89.

VIRGINIA

BEAD GARDEN & HERBARY

11304 Boxwood Road
Fredericksburg, VA 22408
Phone: 703-898-4973
Hours: Call for appointment
Owner: Tricia Ann Brennan
Specialty: French flower beading

Payment: Cks
Retail: Yes
Wholesale: Yes
Mail Order: Yes
Classes: Call for schedule
Custom Work: Yes

The Bead Garden designs and makes beaded flowers, jewelry and holiday ornaments. They also sell bead flower supplies, seed beads and offer instruction in flower beading.

THE BEAD SHOP

10222 Warwick Boulevard
Newport News, VA 23601
Phone: 804-591-0593
Hours: Mon 11-4 Tues-Sat 11-6
  Wed 11-8
Owners: Pat Whitley

Payment: Cks-MC-Visa
Wholesale: 10% w/resale no.
Retail: Yes
Mail Order: Yes
Restringing: Call for quote
Classes: Call for schedule
Specialty: Wide variety

All kinds of beads, seed, European glass, Chinese, trade, etc. and constantly searching for unusual beads and components. Also books, tools and many findings. Local and visiting teachers give weekly classes.

BEADS & ROCKS

335 Virginia Beach Boulevard
Virginia Beach, VA 23454
Phone: 804-428-9824
FAX: 804-428-5671
  800-93-BEADS Wholesale only
Hours: Mon-Wed 10:30-6
  Thurs-Sat 10:30-9 Sun 12-6
Owner: James Goldstein

Payment: Cks
Retail: Yes
Wholesale: $100 minimum
Mail Order: $30 minimum
Classes: Call for schedule
Custom Work: Yes
Finished Pieces: Yes

Specialty: Antique glass beads
Exhibiting at: many bead bazaars and shows, call for current schedule

Retail bead store and sales at nationwide bead and glass shows. Specializing in antique glass beads, stones and buttons, plus other beads from around the world. Also jewelry quality gems and closeouts.

BEADAZZLED

1961 Chain Bridge Road
Tysons Corner Center
McLean, VA 22102-4562
Phone: 703-848-2323
FAX : 301-608-0518
Hours: Mon-Sat 10-9 Sun 12-5
Owners: Penny and Erik Diamanti deWidt
Specialty: Quality beads

Payment: Cks-MC-Visa-AE
Retail: Yes
Mail Order: Yes
Catalog: $5
Custom Work: Yes
Finished Pieces: Yes

Beads of every sort from everywhere with beads for collectors and beginners in this well-lit, inspiring environment. Antique, contemporary, ethnic, gemstones, glass, sterling, 14K, gold filled, brass, copper, amber, coral, clay, porcelain and plastic. Seed beads, fetishes, amazing selection of strands: trade beads, Czech and Indian glass. Knowledgeable and helpful staff and free how-to handouts. Wide selection of findings, stringing materials and bead books. Their goal is to help unleash your creativity and direct importing keeps the prices down.

STAR'S BEADS
2433 Rockbridge Street
Vienna, VA 22180
Phone: 703-698-0626
Hours: Monday 12-8
Owner: Star McGivern
Specialty: Classes
Exhibiting at: Washington D.C. Bead Society Bead Bazaars May and November.

Payment: Cks
Retail: Yes
Wholesale: $200 minimum
Classes: Call for schedule
Finished Pieces: Yes

Star teaches bead stringing and other jewelry making classes. Beads and supplies are sold at the classes.

TOUCH THE EARTH
163 S. Main Street
Harrisonburg, VA 22801
Phone: 703-434-2895 or 432-6289
  or 800-828-9868
FAX: 703-249-4109
Hours: Mon-Fri 10-5 Sat 10-4
Owners: J Scott Eutsler and
  Kay Horton
Specialty: Seed and antique beads
Exhibiting at: Many bead society bazaars and national rendezvous, call for current schedule.

Payment: Cks-MC-Visa-AE
Retail: Yes
Wholesale: Yes
Mail Order: Yes
Catalog: Free brochure
Custom Work: Yes
Finished Pieces: Yes
Consignment: Call for details

Begun in 1977 as a lapidary supply store in LaCross, Wisconsin. The local Native American population frequented the shop and their requests for supply items began Touch The Earth's association with the bead business. In 1987 a store was opened in Harrisonburg, Virginia. Though the Virginia store still supplies the Native American market with beads and supplies through mail order and at powwows, their travel abroad has increased the offerings and allowed them to include ancient, antique and ethnic beads from around the globe in the ever expanding inventory. Also beading supplies, thread, needles, books, looms and findings.

BEAD BAZAAR

1200 Harris Street #302
Bellingham, WA 98225
Phone: 206-671-5655
Hours: Mon-Sat 10-7 Sun 12-6
Owner: Elisa Shafa
Specialty: Ethnic

Payment: Local Cks-MC-Visa
Retail: Yes
Wholesale: $100 minimum
Mail Order: Yes
Restringing: Yes
Classes: Call for schedule

A large selection of glass and metal beads, bugles and seeds (5°-14°), wood, Fimo, porcelain and semi-precious. They assist people in designing their own jewelry by providing free written material on the most popular designs as well as samples, demonstrations and classes.

BEAD BOPPERS

11224 Meridian East
Puyallup, WA 98373
Phone: 206-848-3880
Order Line: 800-944-2980
Hours: Mon-Fri 10:30-7 Sat 10-6
   Sun 12-4
Owner: Debbie Christenson
Specialty: Great selection

Payment: Cks-MC-Visa-AE
Retail: Yes
Mail Order: $15 minimum
Catalog: $2.50
Classes: Call for schedule
Restringing: Call for quote

They strive to have the best variety available. New to the business, they know how important it is to have fair prices and excellent variety. New catalog and excellent service. All kinds of beads from all over the world, findings, books, bead kits, Fimo, tools and a great variety of charms.

THE BEAD FACTORY

621 Broadway East
Seattle, WA 98102
Phone; 206-328-7047
FAX: 206-328-7053
Hours: Mon-Sat 10-9 Sun 11-6
Owners: Viki and Mark Lareau
Exhibiting at: Northwest Bead Society bazaars.

Payment: Cks-MC-Visa
Retail: Yes
Wholesale: $25 minimum
Mail Order: Yes
Catalog: $2
Classes: Call for schedule

Concentrating on carrying a large selection of findings, thread and bead supplies in addition to thousands of beads from around the world.

THE BEAD STORE

222 E. Main Street #I
Auburn, WA 98002
Phone: 206-939-9109
FAX: 206-804-6875
Hours: Mon-Sat 10-6
Owners: Harlan Meier and Kerri Olsen

Payment: Cks
Retail: Yes
Mail Order: $10 minimum
Classes: Call for information

A fun shop designed to cater to the hobbyist looking to enhance their personal adornment. A wide variety of beads from around the world, tools for making jewelry in the store and lots of books.

BEADED TOUCAN

1504 Lampard Road
Friday Harbor, WA 98250
Phone; 206-378-5180, 800-851-5853
FAX: 206-378-5138
Hours: Mon-Fri 8-5
Owners: Bob and Bonnie Oldwyn
Specialty: Great service
Exhibiting at: Call for dates and locations

Payment: Cks-MC-Visa
Retail: Yes
Wholesale: Yes
Mail Order: Yes
Catalog: Free

Great selection of beads including Mexican, stone, glass, metal and plated, sterling, wood and clay. with a continually growing assortment of findings, cording and thread. Direct importers of Mexican Indian beads, specializing in Jaboncillo beads available in 14 colors, "primitive" masks, crosses, terra cotta and black clay fetishes, plus black clay whistles.

BEADS & BEYOND INC.

25 -102nd Avenue N.E.
Bellevue, WA 98004
Phone: 206-462-8992
FAX: 206-453-9116
Hours: Mon-Sat 10-6 Sun 11-3
Owner: Peter and Kathryn Dannerbeck
Specialty: Great selection

Payment: Cks-MC-Visa
Retail: Yes
Wholesale: Very limited
Mail Order: Yes
Classes: Call for schedule

A full service bead store offering over 6,000 types of beads, books, tools and findings. Peruse the beads in a well lighted very organized store that believes in customer service. A wide variety of classes offered weekly featuring both local and guest instructors. Classroom space is adjacent to the store, providing a comfortable workspace condusive to beading with easy access to thousands of beads. Workspace is also available in the 2,100 sq. ft. store. The customers love this store.

BEADS INDEED!

2829 NW 58th Street
Seattle, WA 98107
Phone: 206-784-6484
Hours: Wed 1-7, other times
  by appointment
Owner: Robin Atkins
Specialty: European pressed glass and lampworked beads

Payment: Cks
Retail: Yes
Wholesale: Yes
Mail Order: Yes
Classes: Call for schedule
Custom Work: Yes

Robin offers something a little different: a private studio/shop where you can sit comfortably and ponder over a large selection of beautiful and unique beads, plus a stimulating environment where small groups of creative people gather to take workshops in professional beading and metalsmithing techniques. Caters to serious beaders, artists and collectors (no plastic or plated metal). Direct importer of European pressed glass and lampworked beads. Best selection of trade beads in the area, glass buttons and many more unusual things.

BRITZ BEADS

608 W. Garland Avenue
Spokane, WA 99205
Phone: 509-324-8770
FAX: 509-489-5077
Hours: Tues-Sat 11:30-5
Owner: Sandi Britz
Specialty: Philippine beads

Payment: Cks
Retail: Yes
Finished Pieces: Yes

This retail business is an offshoot of their mail order wholesale bead business. Sandi is an exclusive sales rep for Kalipay Philippine Beads, including horn, shell, heishi, wood, brass and buttons. Also Japanese and Czech seed beads, contemporary handmade beads from artists around the country, tools, looms and wire.

THE GARUDA & I

60 First Street
Friday Harbor, WA 98250-2723
Phone: 206-378-3733
Hours: Mon-Sat 10-5 Sun 12-5
Owners: Whitney Peckman
Specialty: Ethnic beads

Payment: Cks-MC-Visa-AE
Retail: Yes
Wholesale: $50 minimum
Mail Order: $10 minimum
Finished Pieces: Yes

A bead shop and an ethnic art gallery. More than 2,500 different types of beads and findings displayed in a warm and pleasant atmosphere to stimulate your creativity. Lots of glass beads including contemporary lampworked beads. New and old trade beads, gold, silver, seed, and wood beads, an impressive selection of exotic and specialty beads.

HANDS OF THE HILLS

3016 - 78th Avenue S.E.
Mercer Island, WA 98040
Phone: 206-232-4588
FAX: 206-236-9009
Hours: Mon-Fri 9-5

Payment: Cks-MC-Visa
Wholesale: $50 minimum
Mail Order: $50 minimum
Catalog: $5
Finished Pieces: Yes

Owners: Duangporn and Steven Dunning
Specialty: Thai/Khmer silver beads, Peking glass, white hearts
Exhibiting at: California, San Francisco and Seattle Gift Shows

Exceptional and rare trade beads from China, Tibet, Nagaland, and
Southeast Asia, Peking glass (new and old), Southeast Asian trade
beads, and old white hearts. Excellent and fast service for wholesale
catalog orders. They have a large selection of quality beads. Prices are
low and customers receive free newsletters with information about the
owners various trips as well as the merchandise they carry.

147 Washington

ISLAND BEADS AND MORE

3016 - 78th Avenue S.E.
Mercer Island, WA 98040
Phone: 206-232-8121
FAX: 206-236-9009
Hours: Mon-Fri 10-7 Sat 10-5
  Sun 12-5
Owners: Duangporn and
  Steven Dunning
Specialty: Ethnic beads

Payment: Cks-MC-Visa
Wholesale: $50 minimum
Mail Order: Yes
Retail: Yes
Finished Pieces: Yes
Classes: Call for schedule
Restringing: Call for quote

Almost 10,000 types of beads are beautifully displayed in this store where professional and friendly service is readily available. A comprehensive collection of beads, tools, components and findings. The owners travel abroad to purchase beads and bring back an extensive collection of folk art and textiles which are also for sale. Beads include glass, horn, wood, metal, ceramic, Fimo, porcelain and too many others to mention. You'll feel comfortable and welcome at this store and want to spend the day picking out beads and ethnic art to take home.

MARGIE'S DESIGN

10020 A Main Street #411
Bellevue, WA 98004
Phone: 206-723-6483
Hours: Mon-Tues 12-8 Wed 12-9
  Thurs 8-6 Fri 12-8 Sat 8-8
Owners: Margaret Sutter
Specialty: Semiprecious beads
Exhibiting at: Northwest Bead Society bazaar, October 1995

Payment: Cks
Retail: Yes
Wholesale: Yes
Finished Pieces: Yes
Restringing: Call for quote
Custom Work: Call for quote

Margie creates and sells her own jewelry designs from sterling silver beads, semiprecious stones and antique buttons. She also sells seed beads, ethnic beads, found objects, turquoise and wood block prints.

MONSOON

4536 University Way N.E.
Seattle, WA 98105
Phone: 206-633-2446
FAX: 206-634-2420
Hours: Mon-Fri 10-7 Sat 10-6 Sun 12-6
Owners: Eric and Nancy Gorbman

Payment: Cks-MC-Visa-AE
Retail: Yes
Wholesale: $150 minimum
Mail Order: Yes
Catalog: $10 wholesale only

Wholesale Hours: Mon-Fri 9-5

Direct importer of beads from all over Asia. Importing tons of glass beads from India, Taiwan and Indonesia. Beads are sold wholesale to stores nationwide and there is also a retail store that sells a lot of Czech glass, semiprecious, antique seed beads, new seed beads, pony, Crow and bugle beads.

NORTHWEST PASSAGE, INC.

206 Burwell Street
Bremerton, WA 98337
Phone: 206-377-9849
Hours: Mon-Sat 10-6 Sun 11-5
Owner: Corinne Kalb
Specialty: Native American

Payment: Cks-MC-Visa-AE
Retail: Yes
Wholesale: Yes
Mail Order: Yes
Catalog: Free
Classes: Call for schedule
Restringing: Yes

Primarily a Native American/Mountain Man crafts and supplies source. Two locations at present and two-four people work at shows acorss the U.S. Also a full-service mail-order company featuring the work of many craftspeople, both Native American and others, with items representing many tribes. The beads and supplies and jewelry findings are based on the needs of the Native American but they do carry an array of non-traditional items from faceted Austrian crystal to fresh water pearls to Japanese 15° hex.

OUTRAGEOUS TEMPTATIONS BY ALIBECK

P. O. Box 1492
North Bend, WA 98045
Phone: 206-888-1509
Hours: Mon-Fri 10-5 Sat 11-4
Owner: Alibeck
Specialty: Costume for Middle
   Eastern dance

Payment: Cks
Retail: Yes
Wholesale: $50 minimum
Mail Order: Yes
Classes: By appointment
Finished Pieces: Yes

Alibeck is a costume designer, artist, and author of the book "*Be-Dazzling! Hand Beading Techniques for Clothing & Costumes*" and she teaches hand beading on fabrics.

PACIFIC CROSSROADS

238 Taylor Street
Port Townsend, WA 98368
Phone: 206-385-5011
Hours: Mon-Sun, call
Owner: Margaret Schermerhorn

Payment: Cks
Retail: Yes
Consignment: Call for details
Restringing: Call for quote
Custom Work: Call for quote

A small shop that reflects the varied tastes of its owner, who spends half her life within its ever-changing confines and produces one-of-a-kind necklaces, bracelets, hairclips and brooches, called "Margaret's Collection", sold by her rep to a variety of fine shops in Washington and Hawaii. The stock of beads and findings reflects the style of her work, rather than being a fully stocked bead emporium and includes beads from around the world and from local artists. Folk art, Chinese pottery and unique Navajo and Zuni art.

RINGS & THINGS

814 W. Main Street
P. O. Box 450
Spokane, WA 99210
Phone: 509-624-8565, 800-366-2156
FAX: 509-838-2602
Hours: Mon-Sat 9:30-6 Sun 11-5
Owner: Russ Nobbs
Exhibiting at many craft and gift shows, call for schedule

Payment: Cks-MC-Visa
Retail: Yes
Wholesale: $50 minimum
Mail Order: $50 minimum
Catalog: $2
Restringing: Call for quote
Finished Pieces: Yes

Two divisions, the wholesale mail order division imports hairpipe and glass beads from India, supplies professional craftspeople with high quality domestic jewelry findings, in addition to inexpensive findings from Hong Kong; bead and bead books, earring cards, display and plastic locking bags. The retail division is Spokane's 20 year old secret. The bead room is fill with old and new beads from all over the world, basic seed beads, exotic African and Asian trade beads, glass, metal, wood, porcelain, enamel, gemstone, heishi, trade and very little plastic, plus all the parts and findings to make beads into jewelry. The Bead Room is not catalog compatible --too many beads are one of a kind and are best hand picked.

SHIPWRECK BEADS

2727 Westmoor Court SW
Olympia, WA 98502
Phone: 360-754-BEAD (2323)
FAX: 360-754-2510
Orders Only: 800-950-4232
Hours: Daily 10-6
Owner: Glenn Vincent
Specialty: World's largest selection of beads.
Exhibiting at: Tyson Wells Sell-A-Rama, Western Washington Fair, September 1995 under the Grandstands.

Payment: Cks-MC-Visa
Retail: Yes
Wholesale: $25 minimum
Mail Order: $25 minimum
Catalog: $4
Finished Pieces: Yes
Restringing: $15/hour
Custom Work: $15/hour

Established in 1969 they have been serving people all over the world with beautiful, practical and unique beads. Retail, wholesale and distributor pricing available. Director importer of Czech beads and they also import from India, the Philipines, Austria and the Far East. Thousands of beads in every size, shape, color and material imaginable and a large selection of findings. The store is very large (4,000 sq. ft.) and you'll have a lot of fun looking through all the great beads and the bargains there. They also sell cords, books, beading supplies and finished earrings. This is one bead store you won't have trouble finding, their huge sign seems to float in the sky and leads you right to the beads.

THE BLUE BEAD

1931 Monroe Street
Madison, WI 53711
Phone: 608-251-2583, 608-251-0520
Hours: Mon-Fri 10-6 Sat 10-6 Sun 12-4
Owners: Ellyn Zografi and Ramsey Finger

Payment: Cks-MC-Visa
Retail: Yes
Mail Order: Yes
Classes: Call for schedule

They emphasize both the design possibilities of the beads and their importance in the history of trade and culture. A large selection of beads and ornaments, both old and new, from around the world as well as the findings and materials to put your creations together. A well-stocked library of both in-store reference materials and books for sale.

KNOT JUST BEADS

8000 W. National Avenue
West Allis, WI 53214
Phone: 414-771-8360
Hours: Tues-Thurs 10-6 Fri 10-3
   Sat 10-4
Owner: Kim Rueth

Payment: Cks-MC-Visa
Retail: Yes
Mail Order: $20 minimum
Catalog: Yes
Classes: Call for schedule
Restringing: Call for quote
Specialty: Vintage glass

Opened in 1993 to cater to the serious bead enthusiast. Beads from around the world, Japanese and Czech seed beads, *delicas*, vintage, Bali silver. They are constantly searching for new sources of vintage glass and semi-precious stone to be able to supply customers with the best possible selection. Design assistance offered and information gladly given. Also books, finished pieces, stringing materials, findings, charms and tools.

LULU'S BEADS

The Avenue Mall
10 College Avenue, # 125A
Appleton, WI 54911
Phone: 414-734-2323
FAX: 414-734-2424
Owner: Debra Orton

Payment: Cks-MC-Visa
Retail: Yes
Wholesale: $100 minimum
Mail Order: $50 minimum
Classes: Yes
Hours: Mon-Fri 10-8 Sat 10-5

Big, bright colorful shop in downtown mall with a large selection of beads and findings from around the world. Also African art and fabric.

PLANET BEAD

714 N. Broadway
Milwaukee, WI 53202
Phone: 414-223-4616, 800-321-6120
Hours: Mon-Sat 11-6
Owners: Sharon and Keith Seib

Payment: Cks-MC-Visa
Retail: Yes
Wholesale: $100 minimum
Mail Order: Yes
Catalog: $3
Restringing: $5 and up

Located in the heart of downtown Milwaukee, the store is easy to reach, just north of Wisconsin Avenue. A large selection of beads and finished jewelry. Also handmade findings, crystals, textiles, and books.

TROPIC JEWEL

449 State Street, #F
Upper Level
Madison, WI 53703
Phone: 608-256-4442
Hours: Mon-Fri 10:30-7
  Thurs till 8 Sat 10-6 Sun 11-5
Owner: Dennis Koberstein

Payment: Cks-MC-Visa
Retail: Yes
Wholesale: $100 minimum
Mail Order: $50 minimum
Designer Discount: 15%
Classes: Call for schedule
Finished Pieces: Yes
Specialty: Czech beads

Incredible variety and low prices offered in the retail store. Importer and wholesaler of beads from all over the world. Lots of Czech and Indian glass, Venetian, Thai/Khmer, metal, seed and bugle beads. Thousands of styles of sterling silver jewelry and unique gift items.

TURTLE ISLAND BEADS

S 3715 Fairfield Road
Baraboo, WI 53913
Phone: 608-356-8823
FAX: 608-356-5800
Hours: Mon-Tues 9-4 Wed 9-8
  Thurs-Fri 9-4
Owners: Dick and
  Diane Steffensen

Payment: Cks-MC-Visa
Retail: Yes
Wholesale: Yes
Mail Order: Yes
Catalog: $3.50
Finished pieces: Yes
Classes: Call for schedule
Restringing : Yes

Specialty: Bugle and seed beads
Exhibiting at: Midwest pow wow circuit, call for schedule

A vast selection of Czech seed and bugle beads in most sizes and colors, old time color French seed beads, white hearts, pony beads, findings, leather and a complete bead craft book selection. Also Native American dance bells, jingle, conchos, findings and looms.

These beads are a selection of the many great beads entered in the Cover Bead Competition. See page ii, The Beadmakers, for a list of the beadmakers shown here and for information on how to order a copy of this photo.

153

*Tropical fish
Harmon Schmelzenbach*

*Kate Fowle
Lampworked glass beads*

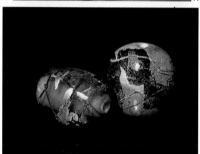

*René Roberts
Lampworked glass beads*

*Self-portrait, Cynthia Toops
Polymer Clay
3rd Place Winner
Cover Bead Competition*

154

Lucy Bergamini
Chevron bead

4th Place Winners
Cover Bead
Competition

Donna Milliron
Pate De Verre
bead

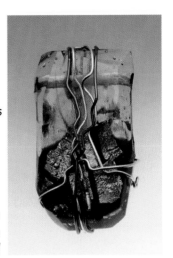

Crystal Myths, Inc

Glass Gallery/School
Proprietor
Lewis C. Wilson

*"The P.T. Barnum
of glass beadmakers"*

Glass Sculptures
Beads
Marbles
Glass Buttons
Glass Bracelets

Videotapes on
glass beadmaking
and sculptured glass
Catalog…$6.00

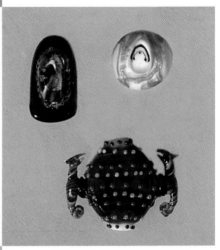

Crystal Myths, Inc

#8 Patio Market
Old Town
Albuquerque, New Mexico
87104
505-246-1606 Gallery/School
505-883-9295 Studio

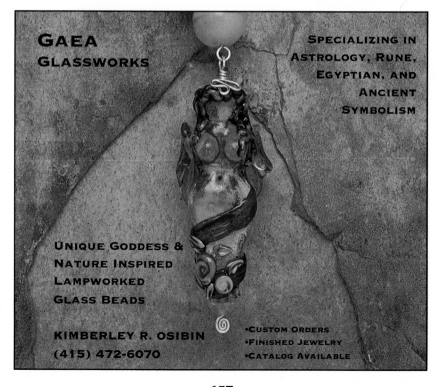

158

Handmade Sterling Silver and Carved Beads
Silver Charms, Pendants, Unique Necklace Clasps

nina
designs

Catalog Available: Please Specify Wholesale or Retail
PO Box 5766, Santa Fe, NM 87502   1-800-336-6462 or 505-982-1214

160

164

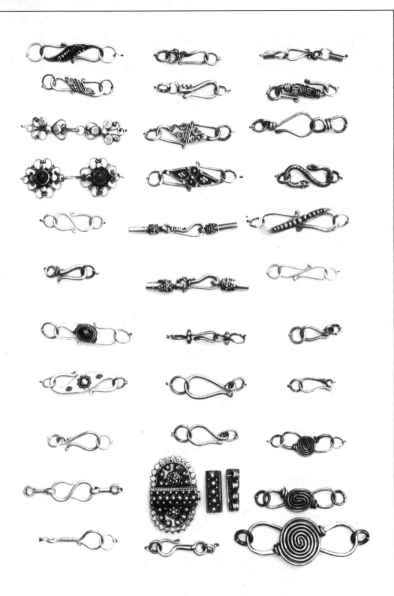

165 Mail Order

These businesses sell through mail order and at trade shows and, if noted, some may schedule appointments in their showrooms.

THE BEAD ROOM
P. O. Box 972
Streamwood, IL 60107
Phone: 708-213-7510
Hours: Daily 9-5

Payment: Cks
Retail: Yes
Wholesale: $200 minimum
Mail Order: $100 minimum
Catalog: No

Owners: Wilma Wilson and Laura Chatain
Specialty: Glass beads only
Exhibiting at Chicago Midwest Bead Society bazaars and other shows all over the Midwest. Call for current schedule.

An exceptional collection of vintage, handmade, and new glass beads.

CHRISTINA'S DESIGNS
P. O. Box 3852
Manhattan Beach, CA 90266
Phone: 310-644-5106, 800-964-2323
Hours: Call

Payment: Cks-COD
Retail: Yes
Wholesale: $75 minimum
Mail Order: $100 minimum
Catalog: Yes

Owners: Christina Lopez, Jim Bourget
Specialty: Swarovski Austrian crystal beads in 27 colors.

Swarovski Austrian crystal such as beads, pendants, suncatchers, flatbacks and rhinestones. Also gold filled and sterling jewelry findings. They will help you find exactly what you're looking for with their quick and friendly service.

COLUMBINE BEADS
2723 Loch Haven Drive
Ijamsville, MD 21754
Phone: 301-865-5047, 800-638-6947
FAX: 301-865-1016
Hours: Mon-Fri 9-9 by appointment

Payment: Cks-MC-Visa
Retail: Yes
Wholesale: One kilo min.
Mail Order: Yes
Catalog: $3.50

Owner: Linda Agar-Hendrix
Specialty: Japanese and Czech beads
Exhibiting at: Many bead society sales, call for current schedule.

A retail company with emphasis on personalized customer service with fast turnaround on orders. Out of the ordinary beads and high quality Japanese beads, matte AB, hex, triangle and square, some custom colors, also 3-cut Czech beads, lampworked Venetian and beading supplies such as hardwood looms, needles and Nymo.

EMPYREAN BEADS

7129 34th Avenue S.W.
Seattle, WA 98126-3301
Phone: 206-937-4146
FAX: 206-932-1332
Hours: By appointment
Owner: Ms. Sammie A. Pullen
Specialty: Seed beads to size 22
Exhibiting at Northwest, Portland, and Northern California Bead Society bazaars.

Payment: Cks-MC-Visa
Retail: Yes
Mail Order: Yes
Catalog: $2 refundable
Classes: Call for information

Mail order company that specializes in new and old seed beads from size 11 to size 22 such as Japanese beads (delicas 11°, 15° hex 11° and 15° round and bugles), Czech seed beads; French size 12° to 15° and vintage Italian beads 18°-22°, as well as Nymo, bead books and needles.

GREY OWL INDIAN CRAFT SALES CORP.

P. O. Box 340468
132-05 Merrick Boulevard
Jamaica, NY 11434
Phone: 718-341-4000
FAX: 718-527-6000
Hours: Mon-Fri 9-5:30
 Sat 10-3 (2nd Sat. of month)
Owner: James Feldman
Contact: Wes Cochrane
Specialty: Native American crafts

Payment: Cks-MC-Visa-AE
Retail: Yes
Wholesale: $300 min. 1st time
Mail Order: Yes
Catalog: $3

A 47 year old mail order company that sells everything to do with Native American Indians including beads, feathers, tapes, books, videos, leather, craft kits, craft tools, ready made beadwork and tipis. Over 4,000 items in all as well as all kinds of beads including seed, cut, wooden, disc, pony, white hearts and old style beads.

HECHO A MANO

P. O. Box 3164
La Mesa, CA 91944
Phone: 619-463-4881
FAX: 619-463-1377
Hours: Mon-Sat 10-6
Owner: Richard Rosenborg
Specialty: Ceramic beads from Guatemala

Payment: Cks-MC-Visa
Retail: Yes
Wholesale: $100 minimum
Mail Order: $100 minimum
Catalog: NO

Distributor of handmade ceramic beads which are produced in their workshop in Guatemala, Central America.

KALIPAY PHILIPPINE BEADS

59 E. Queen #210
Spokane, WA 99207
Phone: 509-487-7161 /800-759-5356
FAX: 509-489-5074
Hours: By appointment only
Owner: Sandi Britz, Sales Rep.
Specialty: Philippine beads

Payment: Cks
Wholesale: Yes
Mail Order: Yes
Catalog: $5

Loi Rosenfeld imports the beads (components, animal fetishes, silver and brass inlaid, shell heishi, and natural woods) from her native homeland, the Philippines. Sandi runs the mail order division that sells all kinds of Philippine beads to bead stores, catalog companies and designers throughout the U.S. Orders sent within one day.

MATERIAL CULTURE

610 Sheldon Drive
Ft. Collins, CO 80521
Phone: 303-221-2084
FAX: 303-484-3684
Hours: Mon-Sat 8-5
Owner: Dirk Ross
Specialty: Cat's eye beads and beads of Asia

Payment: Cks-MC-Visa
Wholesale: $300 minimum
Mail Order: $100 minimum
Sample Card: $6

If you like Miracle beads, you'll like Cat's Eye beads even better and the price is less.

MATOSKA TRADING CO.

P. O. Box 2004
Yorba Linda, CA 92686
Phone: 909-393-0647
FAX: 800-821-0162
Hours: Call
Owner: Brent Schellhase
Specialty: Native American craft supplies
Exhibiting at: Pasadena Indian Show, Pasadena, California, October and March, Southern California Indian Center PowWow, Orange County Fairgrounds, Costa Mesa, 1st weekend in August.

Payment: Cks-MC-Visa-AE
Retail: Yes
Wholesale: $40 minimum
Mail Order: Yes
Catalog: $3

Native American craft supplies and related materials. A complete line of seed beads, needles, thread and other supplies. An extensive selection of books about the Plains Indian including craft how-tos, museum catalogs, photography, history and more. Also Czech beads, pony, crow, metal, seed, modern and "old-time" colors, Peking glass and other beads.

PENNYLANE BEADS

P. O. Box 327
Suisun City, CA 94585
Phone: 707-864-3515
FAX: 707-864-0802
Hours: Mon-Fri 8-6
Owner: Karen Hamilton
Specialty: Great prices

Payment: Cks-MC-Visa
Mail Order: $50 minimum
Catalog: $2

Catalog only business selling glass, horn, metal beads and charms. Great prices, low minimums and sold in quantity discounts for designers and retailers. Pennylane, where your designs make dollars and sense.

RENEE FOXX BEADS BY MAIL

196 Valley Street
Pembroke, MA 02359
Phone: 617-293-4475
Hours: Call for appointment
Owner: J. Shafrin
Specialty: Unusual and unique beads, and a search service.

Payment: Cks-MC-Visa
Retail: Yes
Wholesale: Yes
Mail Order: $15 minimum
Catalog: $3 refundable 1st time or free w/orders over $15

A nationwide mail order source for bead crafters, jewelry designers and anyone using beads for ornamentation and jewelry with low prices and quantity discounts. The catalog is informative and illustrated with photos and drawings and mailed four times a year. Selling semiprecious, glass, metal, enamel, handmade glass, gemstone carvings, seed beads and, acrylic fashion styles. Also instruction kits for jewelry and clothing embellishment and related books.

RISHASHAY

P.O. Box 8271
Missoula, MT 59807
Phone: 406-721-0580
FAX: 406-549-3467
Hours: Call
Owner: John P. Anderson
Contact: Toni Lubrecht
Specialty: Hand made sterling beads

Payment: Cash-MC-Visa
Wholesale: $50 minimum
Mail Order: Yes
Catalog: $3

Wholesale only. Sterling beads, carved Chinese and porcelain.

SAN FRANCISCO ARTS & CRAFTS

1592 Union Street #174
San Francisco, CA 94123
Phone/FAX: 707-935-6756
Hours: Call
Owners: Peter Wiley, Kelly Ladas
Specialty: Czech seed and fire
   polished beads

Payment: Cks-MC-Visa-AE
Retail: Yes
Wholesale: $50 minimum
Mail Order: $50 minimum
Catalog: $3 refundable
   with $50 order

Exhibiting at: 40 trade shows a year, call for current schedule.

Peter and Kelly travel the world extensively in search of rare and unusual beads. As artists themselves they have a keen eye for what is appealing in the world of fashion and jewelry. A constantly changing selection of beads and artifacts from around the world. They also sell colored copper wire kits 16 to 22 gauge and their own hand fabricated gold-filled and sterling silver jewelry. Always, fast, efficient service.

SHREDS AND PATCHES

P. O. Box 126
Buffalo Gap, SD 57722
Phone: 605-255-4605
Owner: Lilah Pengra
Specialty: Porcupine quills

Payment: Cks-Trade
Retail: One price
Mail Order: Yes
Brochure: SASE
Finished Pieces: Yes

Lilah harvests porcupine quills and sells them "as is" or cleaned and sized. The supply is seasonal. She also sells one-of-a-kind jewelry with mixtures of quills, wood, clay, glass and semi-precious stone.

SOFT FLEX WIRE (MIKE SHERMAN DESIGNS)

P. O. Box 80
Sonoma, CA 95476
Phone/FAX: 707-938-3097
Owners: Mike Sherman, Scott Clark
Specialty: Beading wire
Exhibiting at: Write for current list of shows.

Payment: Cks-M.O.
Retail: Yes
Wholesale: $50 minimum
Mail Order: $50 minimum

Mike sells the new soft flex designer beading wire. State of the art technology has given new flexibility to beading wire with 7 strands x 7 wires per strand = 49 wires of strength giving it long term security, strength and flexibility.

UNIVERSAL SYNERGETICS

16510 SW Edminston Road
Wilsonville, OR 97070
Phone: 503-625-2323
FAX: 503-625-4329
Hours: Mon-Fri 10-4 mail order only
Not a retail store - NO WALK INS
Owners: Carol Perrenoud and Virginia Blakelock
Specialty: Modern and antique seed beads, Czech pressed glass
Exhibiting at Portland Bead Society Bazaar November 1995.

Payment: Cks-MC-Visa-COD
Retail: Yes
Wholesale: $100 minimum
Mail Order: Yes
Catalog: $2
Classes: Ask for schedule

This mobile bead store is run by expert beadworkers. They stock the unusual and the highest quality innovative beading supplies. They are currently having pressed glass beads specially made for them in the Czech Republic which is the source of 100s of colors of tiny seed beads in sizes 16 to 22. There are bead cards available to make mail ordering beads easier. They both teach classes all over the U.S. Virginia is the author of the book "*Those Bad Bad Beads*" and the video "*Bead Looming Techniques.*" Carol's video is "*Beaded Peyote Stitch*". Also books, findings, needles, thread, looms and more.

WAKEDA TRADING POST

P. O. Box 19146
Sacramento, CA 95819
Phone: 916-485-9838 /Call late a.m.
Hours: Mail order only
Owner: Cliff Paulsen
Exhibiting at Pasadena Indian Art Show, October. Most 49'r shows at Cal Expo.

Payment: Cks-MC-Visa
Retail: Yes
Wholesale: $100 minimum
Mail Order: Yes
Catalog: $2
Specialty: Native American

Selling merchandise related to the American Indian and the mountain man trade since 1970 including seed and bugle beads, Crow, brass, metal and antique beads.

GLASS BEADMAKERS

"A profound effect occurs when people handle a handmade glass
bead. Combine that feeling with the mesmerizing effect of fire and
molten glass, and you begin to understand the inspiration of the glass
beadmakers. Though small in size, these handmade jewels represent
enormous talent, a large amount of time and effort, and a vast store-
house of technical knowledge." Donna Milliron, Beadmaker.

ANDRE GLASS
P. O. Box 626
2241 Old Day Creek Road
Clear Lake, WA 98235
Phone: 206-856-4518
FAX: 206-856-6843
Hours: By appointment only
Specialty: Handblown, hand fire polished tubing beads
Owner: Tom Andre

Payment: Cks-MC-Visa
Retail: Yes
Wholesale: $300 minimum
Mail Order: $300 minimum
Catalog: Yes

Handblown glass beads and distinctive jewelry made from these
beautiful and colorful glass beads. **See the group photo in the color
insert for a photo of one of Tom's beads.**

ARROW SPRINGS
4570 Tennessee Drive
Shingle Springs, CA 95682
Phone/FAX: 916-677-9482
Hours: By appointment only
Specialty: Lampwork and
  pate de verre beads
Owners: Donna and Craig Milliron
Exhibiting at: Many bead bazaars, call for schedule

Payment: Cks-MC-Visa
Retail: Yes
Wholesale: Yes
Mail Order: Yes
Catalog: Yes
Classes: Call for information
Custom Work: Yes
Finished Pieces: Yes

Distinctive handmade glass and ceramic beads by Donna Milliron.
Fused, Raku, lampwork and pate de verre beads from $1 to $75.
See the color insert for photos of Donna's pate de verre beads.

BEADMAKERS HOLLAND AND SAGE

P. O. Box 112
Mountain View, AR 72560
Phone: 501-269-2231
Hours: Mon-Fri 9-5
Owners: Tom Holland and
Patricia Sage
Specialty: Diversity in styles
Exhibiting at many bead bazaars, call for schedule.

Payment: Cks
Retail: Yes
Wholesale: $250 minimum
Mail Order: $250 minimum
Catalog: $5
Classes: Call for schedule
Finished Pieces: Call for quote

Sage and Tom make a wide variety of the finest lampwound glass beads. Between them they have 12 years of constant beadmaking experience. Their business is founded on a lifetime of love for cultural adornment in all its diverse aspects, especially beads. Sage and Tom's beads cover a range of methods including reproductions of ancient glass beads as well as many original contemporary designs such as elaborate latticino styles, multi layer reflective overlays, sculptural totem fetish beads and others.

BEADZERK!

Box 126
Gillies Bay, British Columbia
Canada VON 1WO
Phone: 604-486-7233
Hours: By appointment
Owner: Fran Feuer and Bruce Thurston
Specialty: Unique glass beads

Payment: MC-Visa
Retail: Yes
Wholesale: Yes
Mail Order: Yes
Finished Pieces: Yes

Fran sells her one-of-a-kind handmade glass beads and finished jewelry, retail and wholesale.

JOEL BLOOMBERG DESIGNS

600 N. Highway 101
Leucadia, CA 92024
Phone: 619-942-0298
Hours: By appointment
Owner: Joel Bloomberg
Specialty: Innovative designs

Payment: Cks-MC-Visa
Retail: Yes
Wholesale: $100 minimum
Mail Order: $100 minimum
Catalog: Yes
Finished Pieces: Call for quote

This is an owner operated business working with individual artists on a one-to-one basis. Custom designs available on request. By producing their own formulas and colors they can offer bead designs not common on the market. Handblown drawn beads including their own formulas of cobalt, aqua and manganese violet glasses, as well as lamps, vases and perfume bottles.

BOHEMIAN ON THE RANGE

2501 Alamo Avenue S.E.
Albuquerque, NM 87106
Phone: 505-247-4041
FAX: 505-247-4046
Hours: By appointment
Owner: Suzanne B. Stern
Specialty: Silver work

Payment: Cks
Retail: Yes
Wholesale: $500 minimum
Mail Order: Yes
Finished Pieces: Call for quote

Suzanne is a jeweler and beadmaker specializing in handwoven fine silver chain work. All of her work incorporates glass (beads or cabochons) with various metals and precious stones. She sells very few individual beads but is happy to work with designers on custom orders.

TOM BOYLAN BEADS

Box 1759
Mendocino, CA 95460
Phone: 707-877-3578
Hours: By appointment
Specialty: Unique glass

Payment: Cks
Retail: Yes
Wholesale: $250 minimum
Mail Order: Yes

Maker of exquisite, unique glass beads that look like gemstones fashioned by nature.

BOUTZ FAMILY GLASSBLOWERS

1400 Market Street/Choo Choo
Chattanooga, TN 37402
Phone: 615-265-6582
Hours: Mon-Sat 10-6
Owner: Donavon Boutz

Payment: Cks-MC-Visa-AE
Classes: Call for schedule

Donavon Boutz, from a family of German/American glassblowers, teaches traditional German colored glass beadmaking (beginning through advanced). Advanced classes specialize in specific decorating techniques such as feathering, millefiore, florals and crystal casing.

TIP: Great reads for inquisitive beadmakers: *Schott Guide to Glass*, Heinz G. Pfaender, Van Nostrand Reinhold 1983; *All About Glass*, Corning Glass Works, 1968, 1984 at the Corning Musuem, and *Glass Science*, Robert H. Doremus, J. Wiley and Sons, 1973. Tip from Suzanne Stern, Designer and Beadmaker.

CD BEADS

2514 E. Spring Street
Seattle, WA 98122
Phone: 206-328-1325
Hours: By appointment
Owners: Cynthia Toops and Dan Adams
Specialty: Unique necklaces of polymer clay and lampworked beads
Exhibiting at: many Bead Society bazaars, call for schedule

Payment: Cks
Retail: Yes
Wholesale: Yes
Finished Pieces: Yes

Dan's lampworked beads combine with Cynthia's polymer clay beads to make unique one-of-a-kind necklaces. Their work is featured in the *New Clay II, Color Trends 1990* and other publications, and is also for sale at many high end galleries across the country. They also sell individual beads and invite people to come to their studio (by appointment only) and share bead experiences.

TIP: "When making twists and latticinos use the leftover thick ends too. Case with a light transparent color and re-twist for a different effect. This can also be done with rose and leaf cane, just case and re-pull. " Kim Osibin, glass beadmaker

CRYSTAL MYTHS INC.

#8 Patio Market - Old Town
Albuquerque, NM 87110
Phone: 505-246-1606 or
  800-873-2323
FAX; 505-889-9553
Hours: Tues-Sat 11-4 Sun 12-4
Owner: Lewis C. Wilson
Specialty: Dragon beads
Exhibiting at: Quartzsite, Tucson Gem & Mineral Show

Payment: Local Cks-MC-Visa
Retail: Yes
Wholesale: $100 minimum
Mail Order: $50 minimum
Catalog: $6
Classes: By appointment

Lampworking for 20 years, Lewis makes unique beads with sculpted overlays of lizards, fish, bugs and animals; very large lampworked Pyrex sculptures; wire wound beads, millefiori beads, gold leaf overlay and totem pole beads -- many one of a kind He also teaches beadmaking using Italian Murretti glass and produces a series of glass beadmaking videos. **See the color insert for photos of some of Lewis' unique beads.**

DANCING RABBIT DESIGNS

3211 Yarwood Way
Sacramento, CA 95833
Phone: 916-922-0860
FAX: 916-648-9936
Hours: Mon- Sat by appointment
Owner: Della Armstrong
Specialty: Lampwork beads

Payment: Cks
Retail: Yes
Wholesale: $200 minimum
Mail Order: $25 minimum
Catalog: $3
Finished Pieces: Call for quote
Custom Work: Yes

Exhibiting at many bead and craft shows, call for current schedule

Della began beadmaking several years ago to supplement her stained glass business, but the beadmaking has taken over and is now her only business. She make unusual beads such as her seasonal line for Easter, Halloween and Christmas and is constantly developing new beads. In her studio you'll find angels, clown caricature bead dolls, white hares, carrots, hearts, and many other unusual beads. The clown consists of 11 different beads and comes assembled to wear as a pendant or can be easily modified to incorporate into a necklace.

LUSTER GLAZED
ROUND — SIX SIZES 8 - 18 MM
HOLE SIZES > 1 MM AND 2 MM
TWELVE COLOR TILE CARD AND PRICE LIST $3.

WHOLESALE ~ RETAIL

HANDMADE PORCELAIN BEADS

SPLENDID LOON STUDIO EST. 1974

726 TUCKERTOWN RD.   WAKEFIELD, RI 02879   (401) 789-7879

FANCY'S

45 Little Elf Drive
Sedona, AZ 86336
Phone: 602-282-6796
Hours: By appointment only
Specialty: Lampwork beads
Owner: Nancy Jones

Payment: Cks
Retail: Yes
Wholesale: Yes
Mail Order: Yes
Finished Pieces: Yes
Beadmaking Classes: Yes
Custom Work: Yes

Exhibiting at: Arizona Bead Society Bead Bazaars, Spring and Fall.

Nancy has such a love for lampworked beads that she can't not make beads. She shares her love of beads by making unique lampworked glass beads and jewelry. Trained at Pilchuck Glass School, Nancy also teaches and displays her jewelry at many galleries and bead shops.

176 Glass Beadmakers

FETISH DESIGNS

Rt. 4 Box 61-H
Santa Fe, NM 87501
Phone: 505-988-1082
Hours: By appointment only
Specialty: Glass charms
Owner: Paul White

Payment: Cks-MC-Visa
Retail: Yes
Wholesale: $50 minimum
Mail Order: $50 minimum
Catalog: LSASE

Fetish charms in glass in a variety of colors. Various animal, heart, star and geometric shapes wrapped with sterling silver wire.

Kris Peterson

Original lampwork & blown glass beads

Rare chevrons & antique Venetian beads

P.O. Box 232, Clarkston, MI 48347
Tel: 810/627/6708   Fax: 810/627/3953

Catalog $4.00

FINELINE STUDIOS INC.

P. O. Box 4318
306-1/2 S. Ridge Street
Breckenridge, CO 80424
Phone: 303-453-2116
FAX: 303-453-1377
Hours: Mon-Sat 10-6
Specialty: Glass cane beads
Owners: Denise Bloch and Kerry Feldman
Exhibiting at: many bead bazaars, call for current schedule.

Payment: Cks-MC-Visa
Retail: Yes
Wholesale: $200 minimum
Mail Order: $200 minimum
Catalog: $10
Beadmaking Classes: Yes
Finished Pieces: Yes

Denise and Kerry make fine handblown art glass, handblown glass bead jewelry and sculpture in their studio in the high country of the Colorado Rockies. They also handcraft colorful glass cane beads. The glass blowing method used is a contemporary interpretation of historical Italian cane and Swedish color overlay techniques allowing for a wide variety of designs, patterns and colors. The studio also exhibits masterworks of 25 American glass artists in addition to their own work.

KATE FOWLE...LAMPWORKED BEADS

5420 Newark Street, N.W.
Washington, D.C. 20016
Phone: 202-966-7747
Hours: By appointment
Specialty: Lampworked glass
Exhibiting at: many bead bazaars,
  call for schedule.

Payment: Checks
Retail: Yes
Wholesale: $100 minimum
Mail Order: $50 minimum
Catalog: $3
Beadmaking classes: Yes
Custom beads: Yes

Kate is a lampworker specializing in custom and one-of-a-kind beads, as well as beads ordered through her catalog. She has a line of lampworked necklaces and frequently produces special orders for her customers. Kate devotes much of her time to teaching and provides all of the equipment and materials necessary for her two-day beginning and advanced classes. **See the color insert for a photo of Kate's beads.**

GAEA GLASSWORKS

P. O. Box 151613
San Rafael, CA 94915-1613
136 Mabry Way
San Rafael, CA 94903
Phone: 415-472-6070
Hours: By appointment only
Owner: Kimberley Rosaleen Osibin
Specialty: Collectable, handmade lampworked glass beads
Exhibiting at: many bead bazaars, call for current schedule.

Payment: Cks-COD
Retail: Yes
Wholesale: $200 minimum
Mail Order: Yes
Catalog: Black/white Free
Color catalog: $3
Beadmaking Classes: Yes

Kim creates collectable, handmade, lampworked glass beads. Her work is featured in bead stores and galleries throughout the United States and she is best known for her unique goddess beads. These works of art represent the great goddesses of the world and incorporate ancient, sacred symbolism. She expresses the beauty of nature, feminine intuition, and spirituality through her garden, romantic floral, scarab, rune and zodiac beads. Kim teaches comprehensive workshops in beadmaking throughout the country and monthly at The Bead Shop of Palo Alto, California. Custom orders welcome. **See the color insert for a photo of Kim's beads.**

TIP: "You can coax glass into a tremendous variety of shapes and forms, but only if it wants to. The way to master hot glass is to give it exactly what it wants, when it wants it." Michael Max, Beadmaker

GARDENS OF GLASS

P. O. Box 151613
San Rafael, CA 94915-1613
12 Bayo Vista Way
San Rafael, CA 94901
Phone: 415-485-1369
Hours: By appointment only

Payment: Cks
Retail: Yes
Wholesale: $200 minimum
Mail Order: $200 minimum
Catalog: $3
Finished Pieces: Yes
Beadmaking Classes: Yes

Specialty: Collectable, handmade, lampworked glass beads
Owner: Leah Katherine Fairbanks
Exhibiting at many bead bazaars, call for current schedule.

Leah has been working with glass since 1982. Her work is inspired by the beauty of nature, the arts of the Impressionist period and Deco style. She is best known for her unique flower designs, sculptural nymphs, latticino, millefiori canes and twists and goddesses. Leah's beads are featured in shows and galleries across the United States and Europe. **See the color insert for a photo of Leah's beads.**

NANCY GOODENOUGH, GLASS ARTIST

P. O. Box 22684
San Francisco, CA 94122
Phone: 415-759-5105
Hours: By appointment only
Specialty: Cast dichroic glass beads

Payment: Cks
Retail: Yes
Wholesale: $150 minimum
Mail Order: Yes
Catalog: $3

Specializing in one-of-a kind cast, dichroic glass, beveled beads. Galleries around the world sell these dramatic beautifully colored beads, pendants, pins and earrings. Jewelry artists buy pieces to integrate into their own work.

GOSSAMER GLASS

927 Yew Street
Bellingham, WA 98226
Phone/Fax: 206-733-3497
Hours: Call for appointment
Owner: Brian Kerkvliet
Specialty: Lampwound glass beads

Payment: Cash-Cks
Retail: Yes
Wholesale: $200 minimum
Mail Order: Yes
Product List: Sample postcard
Classes: Call for schedule

Founded in 1982, Gossamer Glass has always strived to push the limits of glass art. Brian has revived the dormant art of lampwound beads and mosaic cane. He has taught and inspired other prominent beadmakers in the U.S. His beads are limited to special one-of-a-kind pieces designed to please the collector costing from $25-$800.

HARMON/NYALA ENTERPRISES

P. O. Box 1351
Ruidoso, NM 88345
Phone: 505-430-9209
Hours: Mon-Sat 9-5
Owners: Harmon and
Cindy Schmelzenbach
Specialty: Lampworked glass beads
Exhibiting at: Santa Fe Bead Bazaar, June 1995 and other shows, write for schedule

Payment: Cks-COD
Retail: Yes
Wholesale: $150 minimum
Mail Order: Yes
Catalog: Free
Custom Work: Yes

Harmon's work in glass reflects his deep respect for and fascination with nature. His beads are fun and whimsical and very colorful. Many people buy his beads to wear or to display and enjoy over and over again. He has been repeatedly recognized as an award winner in competitions for contemporary handmade glass beads. Especially popular are his unique tropical fish, inspired by years of diving in the Caribbean, Atlantic and Indian Oceans. Harmon now owns and operates a complete glass studio, expanding three times within the last year. Here he tests his creativity, resulting in individual beads or finished pieces designed by his wife Cindy. Harmon is constantly "pushing the edges" within the field of glass art. They offer finished glass jewelry as well as an extensive line of solid glass sculptures. **See the color insert for a photo of Harmon's fish beads.**

TIP: **ALWAYS** properly anneal your beads in an annealing oven.

INNER LIGHT GLASS

511 E. Vassar Avenue
Fresno, CA 93704
Phone: 209-222-9771
Hours: By appointment only
Owner: Ann Winters-Canfield
Specialty: Torch-worked glass beads

Payment: Cks-COD
Retail: Yes
Wholesale: $50 minimum
Mail Order: $50 minimum
Catalog: $2
Classes: Call for information
Custom Work: Call for quote

Ann has been involved in the art glass medium since 1989. She
started in stained glass, going on to glass blowing and fusing. In 1992
she was awarded a grant to study beadmaking at Pilchuck Glass
School. Inner Light Glass studio has since concentrated on creating
unique beads for designers, collectors and bead stores. Each bead is
designed to be a special miniature sculpture, a piece of art whose
history can be traced back thousands of years.

JOHNSTON GLASS

3445 Shinglehouse Slough Road
Coos Bay, OR 97420
Phone: 503-269-7780
Hours: By appointment only
Owner: Joe and DeeDee Johnston
Specialty: Handmade pyrex beads and jewelry components
Exhibiting at: Call for schedule

Payment: Cks
Retail: Yes
Wholesale: $300 minimum
Mail Order: $20 minimum
Custom Work: Yes
Finished Pieces: Yes

Joe and DeeDee have been making Pyrex beads for over 20 years.
They specialize in all kinds of beads and adornments and make small
beads for earrings and huge beads for the collector and everything in
between. Pyrex colors are soft, earthy, natural and brilliantly sparkly.
Beads range in price from $2 - $200 each.

GINGER KELLY

7328 23rd Avenue N.W.
Seattle, WA 98117
Phone: 206-782-3195
Hours: By appointment only
Specialty: Handmade glass beads
Finished Pieces: Yes
Exhibiting at: many bead bazaars,
    write for schedule

Payment: Cks
Retail: Yes
Wholesale: Yes
Mail Order: Yes
Catalog: Yes, written request
Custom Work: Yes
Classes: Call for schedule
Restringing: Yes

Ginger makes handmade glass beads, jewelry designed with sterling
silver and her glass beads and teaches in the Seattle area. Her jewelry
is sold in many galleries and fine gift stores across the country. Great
colors and contemporary designs.

LAUGHING GLASS

P. O. Box 135
Cutten, CA 95534-0135
Phone: 707-443-7233
Hours: Mon-Fri 9-5
Owner: Molly Vaughan Haskins
Specialty: Wonderful kiln formed
  beads and jewelry components

Payment: Cks
Retail: Yes
Wholesale: $50 minimum
Mail Order: $50 minimum
Custom Work: Yes
Catalog: $3
Finished Pieces: Yes

Molly makes and sells unique, graphic, very contemporary kiln formed glass beads in a large range of sizes and shapes. High contrast, primary colors using glass made in the USA. A one-woman shop with limited production, Molly also makes and sells unique kiln formed glass components including figures, animals, amulets, pendants, 2-holed spacers and charms. These are wonderful beads that will help you create a truly unique piece of jewelry. Molly's work has been featured in *Ornament* Magazine. **See the group photo in the color insert for a photo of one of Molly's beads.**

KRISTINA LOGAN - HANDMADE GLASS BEADS

42 Court Street No. 3
Exeter, NH 03833
Phone: 508-388-0006
Hours: By appointment only
Specialty: Beautiful contemporary
  lampworked glass beads
Exhibiting at: many bead bazaars, call for schedule

Payment: Cks
Retail: Yes
Mail Order: $50 minimum
Finished Pieces: Yes
Beadmaking Classes: Yes

Kristina has been making beads since 1990 and her studio is completely devoted to lampworked beadmaking. She studied fine art at the University of New Hampshire and then spent four years working in glass. Kristina spent six months last year traveling the country making and selling beads, and demonstrating and lecturing about the art of glass beadmaking and she still continues to travel to teach and sell her beads. Her workshops focus on the art of mandrel-wound, lampworked glass beads. Each student is supplied with a bench burner, glass rods and all the tools needed to make beads. Kristina's beads have been shown at the Bead Museum and in galleries across the country. **The back cover of the Bead Directory shows a photo of two of Kristina's beautiful beads. Also see the color insert for a photo of Kristina's beads.**

KRIS PETERSON/LUNA BEAD

P. O. Box 232
Clarkston, MI 48347
Phone: 810-627-6708
FAX 810-627-3953
Hours: Mon-Sat 8-6
Owner: Kris Peterson
Specialty: Rare Venetian beads
Exhibiting at: Tucson Gem & Mineral Show.

Payment: Cks-MC-Visa
Retail: Yes
Wholesale: $50 minimum
Mail Order: $50 minimum
Catalog: $4
Classes: Call for schedule
Finished Pieces: Yes

Kris sells an extensive variety of rare, antique Venetian beads and chevrons imported directly from Italy. Orders are accepted for custom-made lampwork and blown glass beads created by their Venetian artisans. Also available are contemporary lampwork beads, unique one-of-a-kind metalwork and glass jewelry designs by beadmaker Kris Peterson. Luna Bead also offers a unique line of Venetian beadforming tools and Moretti dichroic-coated glass. Although most business is conducted via mail order, studio appointments can be made at either the Clarkston, Michigan or Murano, Italy locations.

MODERN ALCHEMY GLASS

3026 N.W. 60th Street
Seattle, WA 98107
Phone: 206-789-0422
FAX: 206-781-4913
Hours: By appointment only
Owners: Michael Max,
  Trina Wright
Specialty: Handmade glass beads
Exhibiting at: Many bead society bead bazaars, call for schedule.

Payment: Cks
Retail: Yes
Wholesale: $250 minimum
Mail Order: $100 minimum
Finished Pieces: Yes
Beadmaking Classes: Yes

Modern Alchemy is a small hot glass studio that specializes in creating unique handmade glass beads. In addition to their one-of-a-kind beads, they also sell a line of glass bead jewelry that includes earrings and pendants. They offer beadmaking workshops for beginning and experienced beadmakers and a video on glass beadmaking. **Two of Michael's beautiful beads are featured on the front cover of The Bead Directory.**

ODYSSEY DESIGNS

4011 Longfellow Street
Hyattsville, MD 20781
Phone/FAX: 301-927-4206
Hours: By appointment only
Owner: Cheryl J. Spence
Specialty: Lampworked glass beads
Exhibiting at: Washington D.C. Bead Society Bead Bazaars

Payment: Cks
Retail: Yes
Wholesale: Yes
Mail Order: Yes
Custom Work: Yes
Finished Pieces: Yes

Cheryl is a glass beadmaker and jewelry designer offering for sale a unique selection of lampworked glass beads. Many of the beads are one-of-a-kind and unlike other lampworked glass beads. She also designs and sells unique jewelry incorporating antique, ethnic, contemporary beads and components. Studio visits by appointment.

OLIVE GLASS

Rt. 2 Box 3196
Lopez Island, WA 98261
Phone: 206-468-2821
Specialty: Handblown glass beads
Owners: Lark Dalton, Corrie Haight
Exhibiting at many bead bazaars, call for schedule.

Payment: Checks
Wholesale: $100 minimum
Mail Order: Yes
Catalog: Yes

Olive Glass began making beads in 1985. Their line includes hand blown glass beads and lampworked beads. They are always making new styles and colors and are known for the high quality and beauty of their beads.

POTEK GLASS STUDIO

1170 River Road
Dresser, WI 54009
Phone: 715-483-9600, 612-332-5842
Hours: By appointment only
Owners: Nancy and Malcom Potek
Specialty: Lampworked beads
Exhibiting at: Chicago Midwest Bead Society Bazaar.

Payment: Cks-COD
Retail: Yes
Wholesale: $300 minimum
Classes: Call for schedule

One-of-a-kind lampworked and kiln-fired dichroic beads and pendants. Beads can be viewed by appointment. The primary influence stems mainly from their surroundings in their secluded country home. This influence can be seen in their dichroic glass pendants which employ both natural and fantastic, colorful landscapes.

PAULA RADKE ART GLASS DESIGNS

1612 Main Street
Morro Bay, CA 93442
Phone: 805-772-5734
Hours: Mon-Fri 9-5
Owner: Paula Radke
Specialty: Dichroic glass beads
Exhibiting at: Call for schedule

Payment: Cks-MC-Visa
Retail: Yes
Wholesale: $100 minimum
Mail Order: $100 minimum
Catalog: Yes

Paula makes handmade wound dichroic glass beads and fused glass cabs, finished jewelry and fused glass home decorative accessories.

RENE ROBERTS

P. O. Box 399
Sebastopol, CA 95473
Phone: 707-823-0321
Hours: By appointment
Specialty: Handmade glass beads
Exhibiting at many bead bazaars, call for schedule of events, no
wholesale at bazaars

Payment: Cks-M.O.
Retail: Yes
Wholesale: To bead stores
Mail Order: $100 min. retail
$200 min. wholesale
Color xerox: $2 /refundable

Rene Roberts has worked in hot glass since 1980 and makes one of a
kind beads having asymmetrical shapes and patterns inspired by the
natural environment. She uses a unique surface treatment technique
with metals and metal oxides to give soft textural colors with metallic
highlights that are reminiscent of Oriental ceramics. These beads are
visually compatible with glass, metal and natural materials and have
wonderful design possibilities. No catalogue or price list. **See the
color insert for a photo of Rene's beads.**

DON SCHNEIDER-HANDCRAFTED GLASS

543 Deer Street
Plymouth, MI 48170
Phone: 313-459-6419
Hours: By appointment
Specialty: Handcrafted glass

Payment: Cks-MC-Visa-COD
Retail: Yes
Wholesale: 12 beads minimum
Beadmaking Classes: Yes
Mail Order: Yes

Don makes lampworked beads both tube wrapped and mandrel
wrapped of borosilicate glass (Pyrex-type glass). Blown glass pieces
such as paperweights, vases and limited sculptural and architectural
pieces. Demonstrations presentations, classes and Christmas ornaments from $10 to $45 also available.

BRUCE ST. JOHN MAHER

P. O. Box 508
Monte Rio, CA 95462-0508
Phone: 707-865-0910
Hours: Afternoons by appointment
Specialty: Odd optical properties of glass

Payment: Cks
Wholesale: $200 minimum
Mail Order: $50 minimum

Bruce makes cast and fused glass with entrained enamel, stained
dichro 3D scenic landscape and treescape "windows", faux amber
bugs and rainbows. A one man show with a lot of studio equipment
manufacturing to the trade since 1968.

IRENE STANT

P. O. Box 632
Farmington, NM 87499
Phone: 505-325-1595
Hours: By appointment only
Specialty: Lampworked glass beads
Exhibiting at: New Mexico Bead Society bazaars, call for schedule

Payment: Cks
Retail: Yes
Wholesale: $100 minimum
Finished Pieces: Yes

Irene makes lampworked glass and kiln fired beads.

HEATHER TRIMLETT STUDIO

8170 La Mesa Boulevard
La Mesa, CA 91941
Phone: 619-460-7855
Hours: By appointment only
Specialty: Lampworked beads

Payment: Cks
Retail: Yes
Wholesale: $200 minimum
Mail Order: Yes
Classes: Individual instruction
Custom Work: Yes
Finished Pieces: Yes

Exhibiting at: Many bead society bazaars, call for schedule.

Heather is an enthusiastic glass artist who uses a unique combination of transparent glass colors and whimsey to create a feeling of being pulled in through the bead. Each treasure is created individually blending the centuried old technique of lampworking with a little magic. **See the group photo in the color insert for a photo of her beads.**

TWILIGHT FIRE

1422 Francke Avenue
Lutherville, MD 21093
Phone: 410-321-4845
Hours: By appointment only
Owner: Inara Knight
Specialty: Glass beads

Payment: Call
Retail: Yes
Mail Order: Yes

Inara makes lampworked glass beads as well as polymer clay beads. She sells her loose beads and finished pieces of jewelry both wholesale and retail, by appointment or at select Bead Bazaars. Most of her beads are one-of-a-kind.

VICTORIA ALEXIS STUDIO

1106 2nd Street #220
Encinitas, CA 92024
Phone/FAX: 619-632-8390
Hours: By appointment only
Owner: Victoria Alexis Tamura
Specialty: Gem-cut dichroic beads

Payment: Cks
Retail: Yes
Wholesale: Yes
Mail Order: Yes
Classes: Call for information
Catalog: $3
Finished Pieces: Yes

Exhibiting at: many bead and crafts shows, call for schedule

Come and see the artist at work at her studio (by appointment only).
Classes ranging from free form peyote seed bead techniques to
metalwork to lampworked beads and fusing with dichroic glass.
Available for sale: hard to find antique Delica beads and hex seed
beads, plus Alexis' one-of-a-kind lampwork, cast and fused beads.

PATI WALTON-BEADMAKER

P. O. Box 260033
Highlands Ranch, CO 80126-0033
Phone/FAX: 303-470-0202
Hours: By appointment
Specialty: Lampworked beads

Payment: Cks-MC-Visa
Retail: Yes
Wholesale: $100 minimum
Mail Order: $100 minimum
Catalog: $3
Classes: By appointment

Exhibiting at: Many bead bazaars, call for current schedule.

Pati makes handmade lampworked beads using both Italian and
American glass. She also sells Venetian blown beads and jewelry.

WINGED WOMAN CREATIONS

P. O. Box 304
Taylorville, IL 62568
Phone: 217-824-9375
FAX: 217-287-7232
Hours: By appointment
Owner: Stevi Belle
Specialty: Handmade glass beads

Payment: Cks
Retail: Yes
Wholesale: $150 minimum
Mail Order: $25 minimum
Custom Work: Yes
Finished Pieces: Yes

One-of-a-kind lampworked glass beads primarily sculptural beads
that are 1-1/2 to 3 inches long. Shapes include vessels, winged
women, owls, hearts and abstract forms. She also sells Japanese matte
finish 6° beads and various other Japanese bugles and E beads. **See
the group photo in the color insert for one of Stevi's beads.**

PAPER BEADMAKERS

JUDITH CONTENT DESIGNS

827 Matadero Avenue
Palo Alto, CA 94306
Phone: 415-857-0289
Hours: By appointment only
Owner: Judith Content
Specialty: Hand-painted paper beads

Payment: Cks
Retail: Yes
Wholesale: Yes
Classes: Call for information
Finished Pieces: Yes

Judith designs neckpieces comprised of her hand-painted paper beads. The neckpieces are multi-stranded collages of paper beads, ethnic beads, selected raw materials such as coral, amber and turquoise, as well as Fimo fabrications and miniature hand-painted fans. Her work is exhibited at galleries and museums including Julie's Artisans, New York, Virginia Breier San Francisco and the California Crafts Museum in San Francisco

POLYMER CLAY BEADMAKERS

CD BEADS

2514 E. Spring Street
Seattle, WA 98122
Phone: 206-328-1325
Hours: By appointment
Owners: Cynthia Toops and Dan Adams
Specialty: Unique mosaic beads
Exhibiting at many Bead Society bazaars, call for schedule.

Payment: Cks
Retail: Yes
Wholesale: Yes

Cynthia makes the most unusual polymer clay beads and combines with Dan's wonderful lampworked beads to make the most unique one-of-a-kind necklaces. Their work is featured in the New Clay II, Color Trends 1990 and other publications and is also for sale at many high end galleries across the country. They also sell individual beads and invite people to come to their studio (by appointment only) and share bead experiences.

MIRABAI ARTS

42 Eastman Street
Concord, NH 03301
Phone: 603-228-2198
Hours: Call
Owner: Mira S. Gerard
Specialty: Polymer clay face and figure beads

Payment: Cks
Wholesale: $100 minimum
Mail Order: $100 minimum
Catalog: $3
Classes: Call for schedule

Mira creates beads from polymer clay and metallic leaf. Her work is original and unique and she finds inspiration in ancient patterns and designs. The faces and figures in the beads are extremely intricate and the gold and silver leaf on the beads adds to the antique quality.

MORE BEADS

9812 Spillway Court
Burke, VA 22015-1835
Phone: 703-323-0206
Hours: By appointment only
Owner: Nancy Bedford-Palumbo
Specialty: Handmade polymer and lampworked beads
Exhibiting at: Northern Virginia Bead Society bazaar.

Payment: Cks
Retail: Yes
Classes: Call for schedule
Finished Pieces: Yes

Focusing on lampworked glass beads and polymer clay beads created by the artist. Nancy sells her own beads, seed beads, findings, finished pieces, fused glass and stained glass pieces. Classes in polymer clay, lampworked glass beads and seed bead jewelry.

NESTING HEART

P. O. Box 2861
Poulsbo, WA 98370
Phone: 206-297-8348
Hours: By appointment only
  Calls only between 10am - 5pm
Owner: Elizabeth Amanda Able
Specialty: Handmade Fimo beads and jewelry
Exhibiting at: Many bead bazaars, call for current schedule

Payment: Cks
Retail: Yes
Wholesale: $150 minimum
Mail Order: $35 minimum
Catalog: $5 includes samples
Custom Work: Yes
Classes: Yes

Elizabeth works at home designing huge millefiore canes. Limited amounts of loose beads are available wholesale or in select bead stores from British Columbia to Florida. Her jewelry is an assemblage of new and old components from around the world and is available in galleries and museum shops. Each bead is a limited edition. She also makes Fimo buttons.

PORCELAIN BEADMAKERS

TYLER HANNIGAN
P. O. Box 91
1510 Pecan Street
Nokomis, FL 34274
Phone: 813-488-4553
Hours: By appointment only
Owner: Tyler Hannigan
Specialty: Handmade porcelain

Payment: Cks
Retail: Yes
Wholesale: Yes
Mail Order: Yes
Catalog: $3
Finished Pieces: Yes

Tyler designs and produces multi-colored handmade porcelain beads which are polished until silky smooth. A selection of these beads is offered to bead shops and professional jewelers. Tyler also designs a series of beads for limited edition jewelry. In the seventies Tyler designed and produced stoneware and porcelain as The Tyler Bead Co. which supplied bead shops in the United States.

NEWCOMB COMPANY
3734 NE 35th Avenue
Portland, OR 97212
Phone: 503-249-1824
Hours: By appointment only
Owner: Howard Newcomb
Specialty: Porcelain exclusively

Payment: Cks-MC-Visa
Retail: Yes
Wholesale: $100 minimum
Mail Order: $25 minimum
Catalog: Sample card $5
Custom Work: Yes

Exhibiting at: Portland Bead Bazaar, November 4-5; Third International Bead Conference, Washington D.C., November 17-19, 1995.

Howard has been producing ceramic beads since 1972 and makes the highest-quality studio-made porcelain beads. Precisely-shaped tile beads in diameters from 2-6mm. Sample card shows the colors and includes loose sample beads. Howard produced commemorative beads for the 1994 Portland Bead Bazaar and is available to do commemorative beads for others.

SPLENDID LOON STUDIO
726 Tuckertown Road
Wakefield, RI 02879
Phone: 401-789-7879
Hours: Call for appointment
Owner: Barbara Briggs
Specialty: Luster glazed porcelain

Payment: Cks-MC-Visa
Retail: Yes
Wholesale: $100 minimum
Mail Order: Yes
Catalog: $3
Finished Pieces: Yes

A small studio that produces handmade porcelain beads in six round shapes from 8-18mm. The beads are decorated with underglaze color a luster glaze. Fancy hand painted beads in limited editions from $3.50 to $15 retail.

JOYCE WHITAKER PORCELAIN
132 Antrim Street
Cambridge, MA 02139-1132
Phone: 617-547-8128
Hours: By appointment
Owner: Joyce Whitaker
Specialty: Sculptured porcelain beads

Payment: Cks
Retail: Yes
Finished Pieces: Yes

Handmade porcelain beads of great variety, beauty and durability. All are glazed in rich, earthy tones and the holes are generally larger than those found in most beads. Some beads are lustred in gold or platinum and relate well to semiprecious beads. Unlike any other contemporary ceramic beads, Joyce makes individually sculptured centerpiece beads designed with human or nature motifs. The beads continually evolve in style and glaze colors and must be seen in the studio to be selected, only by appointment.

WOOD BEADMAKERS

WOOD FORMS
P. O. Box 637
9 Foster Hill Road
Henniker, NH 03242
Phone: 603-428-7830
Hours: Call

Payment: Cks
Retail: Yes
Wholesale: $25 minimum
Mail Order: Yes
Catalog: $2 Bead samples
and SASE for price list

Specialty: Laminated wood beads and buttons
Owner: Mr. Laurie Grob
Handcrafted exotic wood laminated beads. Laurie designs laminated beads and solid wood buttons, which are created in two styles and four wood types; rosewood, buginga, kingwood and zebrawood.

BEADMAKING SUPPLIES

ARROW SPRINGS
4570 Tennessee Drive
Shingle Springs, CA 95682
Phone/FAX: 916-677-9482
Hours: By appointment only
Specialty: Handmade tools and custom kilns
Owners: Donna and Craig Milliron
Exhibiting at: many bead bazaars, call for schedule

Payment: Cks-MC-Visa
Retail: Yes
Wholesale: Yes
Mail Order: Yes
Catalog: Yes

Handmade tools, custom-made kilns and annealers. Mail order business specializing in tools and supplies for bead makers by bead artists for bead artists. They seek out and offer unusual supplies to produce creative effects and carry a full line of glass and glass "enhancers" as well as books, tapes, foils, reducing frits, pixie dust, Sludge mandrel release and anything and everything for beadmakers.

BEAD SUPPLIES INTERNATIONAL
13609 Engleman Drive
Laurel, MD 20208
Phone/FAX: 301-953-1740 or
   301-490-3099
Hours: By appointment only
Specialty: Unique glass beads
Owner: Judith Conway
Exhibiting at: Greater Washington Bead Society bazaars

Payment: Cks-MC-Visa
Retail: Yes
Wholesale: $50 minimum
Mail Order: Yes
Catalog: $3
Classes: Call for information

Judith makes lampworked and fused glass beads and pendants and also supplies graphite button and marble molds; bead making supplies for torch work and unique glass rods for beadmaking.

FRANTZ BEAD SUPPLY
E 1222 Sunset Hill Road
Shelton, WA 98584
Phone: 360-426-6712
FAX: 360-427-5866
Hours: Call
Owners: Michael and Patricia Frantz
Specialty: Glass beads and beadmaking supplies

Payment: Cks-MC-Visa
Retail: Yes
Wholesale: Yes
Mail Order: Yes
Catalog: $6

Patricia makes unique glass beads and Michael sells beadmaking supplies including Moretti glass rods, kilns, tools and instructional books and videos.

Glass has been the most important bead
material for thousands of years. It is fairly
inexpensive to make, can be formed into
almost any shape in an extremely wide pallet
of colors and is reasonably durable and hard.
Beads Of The World, Peter Francis, Jr.

FRANTZ BEAD COMPANY
Glass Beadmaking Supplies

Moretti glass rods, dichroic glass, annealing kilns, torches, tools, supplies, and instructional books and videos. Expert advice from Patricia and Michael Frantz. Ask for our free beadmaking supply catalog.

Bead Supplies

Venetian glass beads. Thai silver beads, pins, pendants, components, and charms. India bone, horn, and glass beads. Handmade glass beads by Patricia Frantz. Catalog $6.00.

E 1222 Sunset Hill Road, Shelton, WA 98584
TEL (360) 426-6712 FAX (360) 427-5866

LAMPWORK BEAD
PATRICIA FRANZ

THE GLASS MENAGERIE

8170 La Mesa Boulevard
La Mesa, CA 91941
Phone/FAX: 619-464-8323
Hours: Mon-Fri 10-6 Sat-Sun 10-4
Specialty: Glass supplies
Owners: George & Donna Yackey

Payment: Cks-MC-Visa
Retail: Yes
Wholesale: Yes
Mail Order: Yes
Catalog: Free quarterly newsletter.

A full line of bead making and fusing supplies, sheet glass and tools. La Mesa is located just east of San Diego. They also carry supplies for kiln work and lampworked beads.

BEADMAKING SUPPLIES!

Glasscraft has your beadmaking supplies. Whether you're already making your own beads or just want to get started — we can help.

We carry a full line of beadmaking supplies, including starter kits.

For more information call or write:

Glasscraft-Inc.

626 MOSS STREET
GOLDEN, CO 80401
(303) 278-4670
FAX: (303) 278-4672

❖*Free Catalog!*
❖*Beadmaking Classes!*

Beadmaking History

"The oldest and most universal way to make a glass bead is to work with hot glass and wrap it around a shaft of some sort to build up the bead. This circular motion should be kept in mind, because the finished bead will nearly aways reveal this twisting action. Any imperfections in the glass, streaks in color or air bubbles, will be oriented so they encircle this perforation. We call these wound beads. There are several ways to wind beads, but there are some techniques common to each." *Beads Of The World*, Peter Francis, Jr.

MERCHANTS OF VENICE

P. O. Box 327
Riderwood, MD 21139
Phone/FAX: 410-252-0486
Hours: Mail order only
Specialty: Moretti glass
Owners: Karen and Jim Hill

Payment: MC-Visa
Retail: Yes
Wholesale: Yes
Mail Order: Yes
Catalog: SASE

They supply Moretti glass for lamp workers.

NORTHWEST ART GLASS

9003 - 151 N.E.
Redmond, WA 98052
Phone/FAX: 206-861-9600
   800-888-4444
Hours: Mon-Fri 8-4:30 Sat 9-1
Specialty: Moretti rods
Owners: Richard Mesmer

Payment: Cks-MC-Visa
Retail: Yes
Wholesale: $50 minimum
Mail Order: $50 minimum
Catalog: $5
Classes: Call for schedule

Moretti rods, beadmaking tools, supplies and classes.

LEWIS C. SMITH

P. O. Box 176
1414 W. 8th
Medford, OR 97501
Phone: 503-772-7671
FAX: 503-772-7631
Hours: Mon-Fri 10-5 Sat 11-2
Specialty: Tools and glass supplies

Payment: MC-Visa
Retail: Yes
Wholesale: Volume discounts
Mail Order: Yes
Catalog: $2

Bead and marble-making supplies, glass rods, torches, books, videos, jewelry and craft tools, bead trays, bead tubes. Also seed, trade and old and new glass beads.

WALE APPARATUS CO.

P. O. Box D
400 Front Street
Hellertown, PA 18055
Phone: 610-838-7047
   or 800-444-WALE
FAX: 610-838-7440
Hours: Mon-Fri 8-5
Specialty: Glass supplies and tools
Owners: Andrew J. Wargo
Exhibiting at: Glass Art Society, Asheville, NC, May 11-14, 1995 and A.G.S.A. Seattle, WA June 23-25, 1995

Payment: Cks-MC-Visa
Retail: Yes
Wholesale: $100 minimum
Mail Order: $50 minimum
Catalog: Free
Beadmaking Classes: Yes

Manufacturer and distributor of artistic and scientific glassworking equipment and supplies. Products range from the Delta beadmaking bench burner to large capacity bench burners, hand torches and custom burners. Professional and beginner beadmaking kits, ovens and kilns, colored glass rods, didymium spectacles, graphite paddles, miscellaneous beadmkaing tools and supplies, books and videos. No beads.

HAWAII

BEAD HEAVEN
120 Hana Hwy, PO Box 519
Paia Maui, HI 96779
Phone: 808-579-9459 or 243-0577
Hours: Mon-Sun 10-6
Owner: Diana Trifoso-Kara
Specialty: Vintage and seed beads
Exhibiting at: Tucson Gem Show at the Rodeway Inn and many other bead shows, call for current schedule.

Payment: Cks
Retail: Yes
Wholesale: $50 minimum
Mail Order: $50 minimum
Catalog: $3.50
Classes: Call for schedule
Custom Work: Call for quote

A well-stocked store filled with 1,000's of different beads in a heavenly setting on the north shore of Maui. Antique and vintage glass is a specialty with an emphasis on Czech seed beads (over 300 varieties and colors). Unique to this store is they carry 20 different kinds of seeds that grow in Hawaii that are gathered locally and hand drilled. Also findings, beading supplies, finished necklaces, always something new, and friendly knowledgeable service.

BEADS OF PARADISE
120 Hana Hwy, PO Box 173
Paia Maui, HI 96779
Phone: 808-579-9459 or 243-0577
Hours: Mon-Sun 10-6
Owner: Diana Trifoso-Kara
Specialty: Beaded jewelry

Payment: Cks
Retail: Yes
Wholesale: $100 minimum
Mail Order: $100 minimum
Classes: Call for schedule
Gallery: Call for criteria
Consignment: Call

A gallery devoted to those who create beaded art. It is the manifestation of a 15 year vision to create a professional outlet in which artists who work in beads can regularly exhibit their work in the Hawaiian Islands. New work is reviewed by the 15th of every month with a minimum of 20 pieces in each installation. Gallery is available daily as a retail store open to the public. All work must have beads as a central element of design.

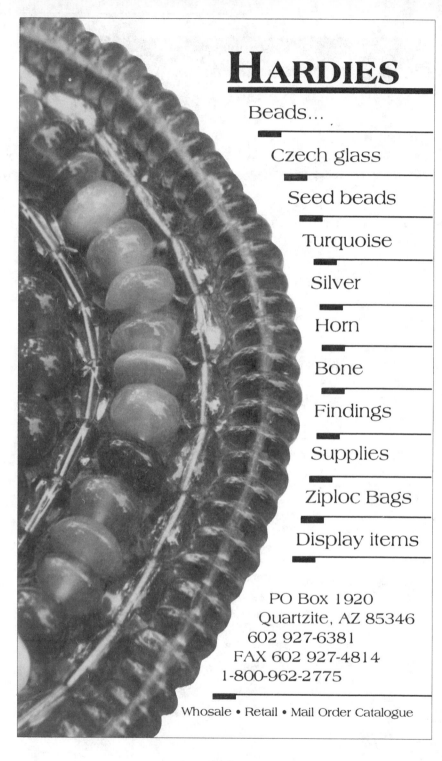

HARDIES

Beads...

Czech glass

Seed beads

Turquoise

Silver

Horn

Bone

Findings

Supplies

Ziploc Bags

Display items

PO Box 1920
Quartzite, AZ 85346
602 927-6381
FAX 602 927-4814
1-800-962-2775

Whosale • Retail • Mail Order Catalogue

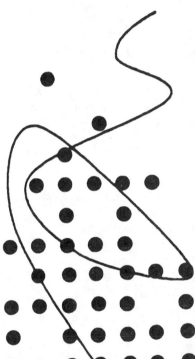
201 Canada

BEADWORKS

126 West 3rd Avenue, 2nd Floor
Vancouver, B.C.
CANADA , V5Y 1E9
Phone: 604-876-6637
FAX: 604-876-3317
Hours: Mon-Fri 9-5
Owner: Graeme Teixeira
Specialty: Large selection

Payment: Cks-MC-Visa-AE
Retail: At retail stores
Wholesale: $50 minimum
Mail Order: $50 minimum
Catalog: $10
Classes: Call for schedule
Custom Work: Call for quote
Restringing: Call for quote

Exhibiting at: Gift Shows in Vancouver and Edmonton,
Canadian Crafts and Hobby Shows in Calgary and Toronto

This is the address for the wholesale office of BeadWorks Canada and
Worldbeads USA. The original BeadWorks shops, now Worldbeads
in the USA sell the largest selection of quality beads from around the
world, findings, leather, books, tools, kits and more. BeadWorks has
13 locations in Canada and seven Worldbeads stores in the USA. All
stores offers classes and beginner jewelry classes are free every
January.

BEADWORKS CANADA

See each listing for address
See each listing for phone number
Hours: Daily 10-6 for all stores
Owner: Graeme Teixeira
Classes: Call individual stores
Custom Work: All stores

Payment: Cks-MC-Visa
Retail: Yes, all stores
Wholesale: Head office
Mail Order: Yes, all stores
Catalog: $10
Finished Pieces: Yes, all stores
Restringing: All stores

Create your own accessories shops. Large selection of quality beads,
findings, leather, books and more.

BEADWORKS   204-452-8762
470-472 River Avenue, Winnipeg, Manitoba R3L 0C8
BEADWORKS   604-983-2309
123 Carrie Cates Court, Lonsdale Quay, No.Vancouver, BC V7M 3K7
BEADWORKS   902-422-1413
1567 Grafton Street, Halifax, Nova Scotia B3J 2C3
BEADWORKS   604-941-7098
2316-2929 Barnet Hwy., Port Coquitlam, B.C. V3B 5R5
BEADWORKS DES PERLES   514-284-6655
2085 St. Denis Street, Montreal, Quebec H2X 3K8

BEADWORKS 604-682-2323
5-1666 Johnston Street, Granville Island, Vancouver BC V6H 3S2
BEADWORKS 403-270-8502
338-10th Street NW, Calgary, Alberta T2N 1V8
BEADWORKS 403-433-9559
10324 - 82nd Avenue, Edmonton, Alberta T6E 1Z8
BEADWORKS 416-693-0780
2154 Queen Street East , Toronto, Ontario M4E 1E4
BEADWORKS 416-763-5446
2326 Bloor Street West, Toronto, Ontario M6S 1P2
BEADWORKS 604-860-1093
140-2271 Harvey Ave., Kelowna, B.C. V1Y 6H2
BEADWORKS 613-562-1238
39 Clarence Street, Ottawa, Ontario K1N 5P4
BEADWORKS 306-653-7033
103-733 Broadway Avenue, Saskatoon, Saskatchewan S7N 1B3

MANO A MANO

313 Queen Street West (at John)
Toronto, Ontario
CANADA , M5V 2A4
Phone: 416-599-3373
FAX: 416-921-6170 (daytime only)
Hours: Mon 12-5
  Tues-Fri 11:30-6 Sat 12-6 Sun 2-6
Owner: Silva Neilands
Specialty: Ethnic and handmade beads

Payment: Cks-MC-Visa-AE
Retail: Yes
Wholesale: Yes, limited
Mail Order: Yes
Catalog: $5
Restringing: Yes
Custom Work: Yes

A small, eclectic business with a constantly evolving selection of high quality beads, pendants, findings, jewelry and folk art. Silva's background is in anthropology and design so her interest lies mainly in handmade and unusual beads from around the world. Lots of antique trades beads, modern African, Czech (old and new), beads from India, China and around the world. Modern items such as Fimo, fabric paints, satin and leather cord and anodized aluminum wire, sheet and ballchain. The folk art selection includes mystic boxes, papeles picados from Mexico, beaded dolls and Zulu beadwork.

THE SASSY BEAD CO.

11 William Street (The Market)
Ottawa, Ontario
CANADA , K1N 9C7
Phone: 613-562-2812
FAX: 613-562-3606
Hours: Daily 10-6 Thurs-Fri till 9
Owners: Natalie Szabo and Greg Best
Specialty: Innovative classes and unique beads

Payment: Cks-MC-Visa-AE
Retail: Yes
Wholesale: Yes
Designer Discount: 20%
Restringing: Yes
Custom Work: Yes

2nd Location: 757 Bank Street (The Glebe), Ottawa, Ontario (613) 567-7886. These stores carry over 10,000 varieties of beads and supplies including Venetian glass, sterling and gold findings, copper, tools, multi-colored leathers and cords and a wide assortment of books. The warm and friendly service will make you want to visit these great bead stores.

SILVER MOON TRADING CO. LTD.

3036 Granville Street
Vancouver B.C.
CANADA , V6H 3J8
Phone/FAX: 604-736-2323
Hours: Mon-Sat 10-5
Owners: Harley & Karen Glesby
Specialty: Ethnic jewelry and bead artifacts

Payment: Local Cks-MC-Visa-AE
Retail: Yes
Wholesale: $250 minimum
Restringing: Yes
Custom Work: Yes
Finished Pieces: Yes

Silver Moon is Canada's premier ethnographic jewelry and bead artifacts gallery. Bead artifacts from around the world circa 2,500 B.C. to the present day, are found in their exclusive "Vanishing Arts Collection, 'Karen' necklaces and 'Luna' earring designs feature ancient, antique and ethnographic beads and artifacts, including rare Tibetan amber, oxblood stone coral, carnelian, turquoise and Dzi, ancient central Asian agates, lapis and jade, ancient Egyptian faience "mummy beads", ancient Phoenician and Roman glass "eye" beads, ojime, Precolumbian turquoise, crystal and terra cotta, fancy African glass trade beads, old silver and much more. Also an extensive collection of related books. **See the color insert for a photo of one of Karen's necklaces.**

BEADS!

259 Portobello Road
London W11 1LR
ENGLAND
Phone/FAX: 0171-792-3436
Hours: Mon-Fri 11-6 Sat 10-6
Owner: Necklace Maker Workshop
Contact: Stefany Tomalin
Specialty: Unusual beads and how-to bead books
Exhibiting at: Bead Society of Great Britain Bead Bazaar, October.

Payment: Cks in Sterling
MC-Visa
Retail: Yes
Classes: Send SASE
Finished Pieces: Yes
Custom Work: Min. charge £5
Restringing: Min. charge £5

Stefany Tomalin, the proprietor, is an author, lecturer, and founding member of the Bead Society of Great Britain. Beads! specializes in unusual, antique, precious, ethnic and handmade loose beads; pendants, threads and fasteners as well as African traditional beadwork. Tuition by appointment. Copies of *Beads!* by Stefany Tomalin for sale in the shop.

SPANGLES

1 Casburn Lane, Burwell
Cambridge
ENGLAND CB5 OED
Phone/FAX: 011-44-638-742024
Hours: Call any reasonable time
Owner: Carole Morris
Specialty: Lace bobbin spangles and Venetian glass beads
Exhibiting at: Bead Society of Great Britain Bead Bazaar, October

Payment: Cks- US or Sterling
Retail: Yes
Wholesale: Yes
Mail Order: Yes
Catalog: Send $1 cash

Mail order and retail bead dealers direct to the public, no shop. Wholesalers of glass and ceramic beads selling glass (especially Venetian), ceramic, metal, semiprecious and stones. Their specialty is bird-cage lace bobbin spangles: beads surrounded by a tiny cage of beads. They also sell lacemaking bobbins and equipment.

MATERIAL CULTURE
. Peitou District
P.O. Box 2-48
Peitou Post Office
Taipei, Taiwan
Republic of China
Hours: Mail order or by appt.
Specialty: Beads of Asia and Taiwan
Contact: Wu Zun-Ci

Payment: Cash - M.O.
Wholesale: $1,000 minimum
Mail Order: $500 minimum
Catalog: $10 samples

Material Culture offers fair prices, good service and excellent acquisition. If it can be found, they have it. When writing, please specify your wants and interests and they will supply photos and prices. They sell beads from Taiwan, China, Burma, Thailand, India, Korea, and Japan as well as bead books and handwoven cloth from South East Asia.

Bead History: "Large quantities of beads were worn by all Tibetans. They were made from the richest materials a family could afford. Thus, Tibet's wealthier urban and village inhabitants generally wore more refined and intricate jewelry than the nomadic peoples, who constituted three-quarters of the country's population. Noble-women wore necklaces of huge amber and coral beads, sometimes almost long enough to reach the ground. Strings of seed pearls were attached to gold prayer boxes inlaid with turquoise and precious stones. The actual value of the jewelry lay not in the precious stones, which were almost always glass simulants, but in the specific components; the intensity of blue in the turquoise set into the face of the charm box; the gold weight of the box; and the size of the red coral and dZi beads of the necklace on which the box was strung." *The History of Beads*, Lois Sherr Dubin.

A brief note about supporting these bead research centers.
The CSB , the CBR and the SBR are the only centers of their kind. They provide important work, researching and publishing books about the beads we all love so much. We recommend that any reader who is able volunteer their time to help these valuable centers continue to do the bead research that benefits us all. Of course a cash donation would always help. Without these centers we would not know as much as we do about the history of beads. Each center is run by one person who has devoted his or her life to their love of beads. **Support them in any way you can.**

Center for the Study of Beadwork

Phone: 503-248-1848
P. O. Box 13719-BD
FAX: 503-248-1011
Portland, OR 97213
Alice Scherer, Director
Membership $20 includes four issues of the quarterly newsletter *notes from a Beadworker's Journal.* 5% discount on book purchases and 10% off on slide kits and postcards.

The purpose of the CSB is to gather and disseminate information on the subject of beadwork. The CSB maintains a study collection, a library, an articles file, and a slide bank, as well as fosters programs of value in the advancement of beadwork. The CSB's study collection includes work from around the world and dating back to the early 1800s. The CSB's library of over 400 books on beads and beadwork and its collection of magazine and newspaper articles is available for perusal on premises to CSB members by appointment.

Single copies of the newsletter are $2.50. Complete sets of back issues are available. Please inquire as to cost. A copy of the CSB's booklist is available for $1 plus a LSASE. This is one of the most informative newsletters available on beadwork.

The Center for Bead Research

Phone/FAX: 518-523-1794
Four Essex Street
Peter Francis, Jr., Director
Lake Placid, NY 12946
Members $30 for two years. All members receive the *Margaretologist* .
Patrons $80 for two years and supporters $200 for two years, also receive new books as they are released. Send SASE for catalog.

Since 1979, the CBR has been dedicated to the study of all beads. The Center maintains the world's largest library on beads, the most comprehensive and best documented bead collection, collections and archives of related interest, permanent and topical displays, a print shop and a small laboratory. The CBR publishes the semi-annual *Margaretologist* containing the latest in bead research around the world. The Center also directs bead conferences, gives lectures, leads bead study trips, sponsors workshops geared for everyone from beginners to professionals, and consults for museums and universities.

Society of Bead Researchers

Formed in 1981 to foster research on beads of all materials and periods, and to expedite the dissemination of the resultant knowledge. Membership is open to all persons involved in the study of beads, and those interested in keeping abreast of current trends in bead research. There are four levels of membership: Individual - $15, $20 Overseas; Sustaining - $35, Patron - $75, and Benefactor - $150. The SBR presently publishes a semi-annual newsletter, *The Bead Forum*, and an annual scholarly journal, *Beads* The Journal of the Society of Bead Researchers. Contents of the newsletter include current research news, requests for information, responses to queries, listings of recent publications, conference and exhibition announcements, and brief articles on various aspects of bead research. Each journal contains 4-5 major articles and several reviews of important publications. Articles and other material for the newsletter and journal are invited and should be sent to Karlis Karklins, SBR Editor, Parks Canada, 1600 Liverpool Court, Ottawa, Ontario, K1A 0M5, CANADA.

The Crafts Center   202-728-9603
1001 Connecticut Ave., N.W., Ste. 1138   Sheila Mooney,
Washington, D.C. 20036   Executive Director

An international, non-profit, membership organization committed to serving the interest and needs of low-income artisans. They provide technical assistance and information to help low-income artisans worldwide achieve and sustain greater quality, productivity and sales.

The National Polymer Clay Guild   202-895-5212
1350 Beverly Road, Suite 115-345
McLean, VA 22101
Annual dues are $20 for individuals, $10 for persons 65 or over and $30 for families.

An organization dedicated to the dissemination of information about the use of polymer clay as an artistic medium. The bimonthly POLYinforMER newsletter contains tips, how-to articles, artist profiles and national workshop schedules. There are also numerous regional groups across the country.

Society of Glass Beadmakers

8170 La Mesa Boulevard
La Mesa, CA 91941

Phone: 619-465-1586
Annual Dues: $30

The SGB is an organization whose purpose is to facilitate networking
among glass beadmakers and collectors, providing opportunities for
members to exchange techniques and information.
Annual gathering: 1995 gathering will be held in Evanston, Illinois
August 3-6.

BEAD SOCIETIES

Bead societies are important. Not only do they serve as a meeting place for beadaholics but they serve to educate members and the public about beads. We all need to attend and pay our dues and volunteer at our bead societies. Also, make sure to attend meetings when you travel. All bead societies welcome guests and you may be able to bring ideas and information back to your own society. If we want to keep the bead business alive and thriving we all need to do our part by supporting our bead societies and realizing the importance of volunteering. If your Bead Society is not listed here, please send complete information.

ALASKA

Juneau Bead Society
Chris Prussing
The Bead Gallery
201 Seward, Juneau, AK 99801

Phone: 907-586-3223
Meetings: First Thursday each month, 7 pm, downtown public library.

ARIZONA

Arizona Bead Society
P.O. Box 80111 Arcadia Station, 072
Phoenix, AZ 85060-0111
Meetings: Third Sunday of each month, 2-4 pm at the Mineral Museum at 15th Avenue and Washington in Phoenix

Phone: 602-839-2695

Tucson Bead Society
P. O. Box 64552
Tucson, AZ 85728
Meetings: Last Thursday of the month, 7 pm, Tucson Boys Chorus Building, 5770 E. Pima Road. Two bead bazaars each year.

Phone: 602-239-3362

Polymer Clay Guild of Arizona
P. O. Box 26124
Tempe, AZ 85285-6124
Contact: Jacqueline James
Meetings: Every six weeks and a newsletter is being planned.

Phone: 602-491-4472
Annual Dues: $15

CALIFORNIA

The Bead Society (Los Angeles)
P. O. Box 241874
Los Angeles, CA 90024-9674
Grants available for bead research
  send #10 SASE for application.
Meetings: First Wednesday each month at 7:30 pm, Fellowship Hall, Westwood United Methodist Church, 10497 Wilshire Blvd., Los Angeles. **Annual Sale**: Twice a year.

Phone: 310-274-3276
Annual Dues: $40, or
$35, Associate Member
  with no voting privileges
Newsletter: Six times a year

Bead Society San Diego County
P. O. Box 230325
Encinitas, CA 92023-0325
Phone: 619-633-1247
Annual Dues: $25
Newsletter: Six times a year
Meetings: Third Wednesday of each month at 7 pm in Mira Mesa.

Northern California Bead Society
1650 Lower Grand Avenue
Piedmont, CA 94611
Deanna Doering, President
Phone: 510-548-4824
Annual Dues: $20
Guest Fee: $3
Newsletter: Quarterly
Meetings: Third Tuesday each month, 8 pm, Holiday Inn, Emeryville.
No December meeting. **Annual Sale**: May.

COLORADO

Rocky Mountain Bead Society
727 Tenth Street
Boulder, CO 80302
Phone: 303-449-1300
Annual Dues: $20
Newsletter: Quarterly
Meetings: Third week of each month at the Arvada Center for the Arts,
6501 Wadsworth Blvd. in Arvada. **Annual Sale**: Next bazaar 1996

DISTRICT OF COLUMBIA

Bead Society of Greater Washington
P. O. Box 70036
Chevy Chase, MD 20813-0036
Phone: 301-277-6830
Annual Dues: $20
Newsletter: Five times a year
Meetings: 2nd Thursday each month at Chevy Chase Community
Center. No August meeting.
Annual sales: May and November. November 1995 they will sponsor
the 3rd International Bead Conference in Washington, D.C.

FLORIDA

Bead Society of Central Florida
121 Larkspur Drive
Altamonte Springs, FL 32701
Phone: 407-831-0843
Annual Dues: $15
Newsletter: Six times a year
Contact: Polly Miller, newsletter editor
Meetings: Monthly meetings and/or workshops are held the 2nd
Monday of each month, Community Room of Fashion Square, Colonial
and Maquire, Orlando.
New Book: An educational monograph: *Early Contact Glass Trade Beads
in Alaska*, by Polly Miller. Includes a pictorial time-line and color
photographs. $15 each or discounts for bulk orders.

Florida West Coast Bead Society
6300 Flotilla Drive #79
Holmes Beach, FL 34217
Phone: 813-778-4705
Irene Murphy
Meetings: First Monday of each month, 7-9 pm at the Selby Library,
1001 Boulevard of the Arts, in Sarasota.

Bead Society of North Florida   **Phone:** (904) 385-3500
c/o Chevron Trading Post   Deborah Coule
2320 N. Monroe Street, Tallahassee, FL 32303
Meetings: Second Tuesday of each month at 7:30 pm at Chevron Trading Post.

Tampa Bay Bead Society   **Phone:** 960-2952
Lydia Borin
P. O. Box 280315, Tampa, FL 33682-0315
Meetings: Third Monday of each month, 7-9 pm, County Center Building, 601 E. Kennedy Blvd, 26th Flr, meeting room A in Tampa.

GEORGIA

Atlanta Bead Society   **Phone:** 404-872-4213
27888 Homeland Drive, Doraville, GA 30340
Meetings: First Thursday of the month at Oglewanagi Gallery, on North Highland Avenue.

HAWAII

Hawaii Bead Society Oahu Chapter
c/o Norma Lanai   **Annual Dues:** $15
95-128 Pipapa Dr. #405, Mililani, HI 96789

Bead Society of Hawaii, Maui Chapter
P. O. Box 12127
658 Front St., #153, Lahaina, Maui, HI 96761
Meetings: Twice monthly, one day meeting is a workshop and one evening meeting is held at a rotating location on Maui.

IDAHO

Coeur d'Alene Bead Society   **Phone:** 208-765-6758
2709 N. Eighth Street   **Annual Dues:** None
Coeur d'Alene, ID 83814   **Newsletter:** Quarterly
Contact: Lisa Hobson
Meetings: First Saturday of the month, 11 am at the Women's Center, 2201 N. Government Way, Ste. E in Coeur d'Alene.

ILLINOIS

Chicago Midwest Bead Society   **Phone:** 708-328-4040
1020 Davis   **Annual Dues:** None
Evanston, IL 60201   **Newsletter:** Quarterly
Contact: Naomi Rubin
Meetings: Second Tuesday of the month 7:30 pm, at Originals, 1020 Davis, Evanston. **Annual Sale:** Holiday Bead Bazaar in November

Bead Society of Greater Chicago
P. O. Box 8103
Wilmette, IL 60091
Judith Schwab, President
Meetings: Second Thursday of month at Salvation Army Community Center, 8354 W. Foster, Chicago.

Phone: 312-714-5455
Annual Dues: $25
Guest Fee: Varies
Newsletter: Quarterly
Annual Sale: September

MARYLAND

The Baltimore Bead Society
P. O. Box 311
Riderwood, MD 21139-0311
Meetings: Second Tuesday of each month at 7:30 pm, Ascension Lutheran Church, 7601 York Road, Baltimore.

Phone: 410-647-93335
Annual Dues: $20
Newsletter: Quarterly

MASSACHUSETTS

Beadesigner International
P. O. Box 503
Lincoln, MA 01773

Phone: 617-499-9432
Annual Dues: $20 New England resident; $15 non-resident
Guest Fee: $3 after first visit
Newsletter: Quarterly

Meetings: Last Wednesday of each month except July, August, December and January at 7 pm at the Belmont Public Library, 336 Concord Avenue, Belmont. **Annual Sales**: Spring and Fall "Bead Affaires"

MICHIGAN

Great Lakes Beadworkers Guild
P. O. Box 1639
Royal Oak, MI 48068
Minneapolis, MN 55401
Meetings: Third Tuesday of every month at 6:30 pm at the Good Shepard Church, 814 N. Campbell Road, Royal Oak. **Annual Sale**: Fall

Phone: 810-634-3649

MINNESOTA

Upper Midwest Bead Society
P. O. Box 4081
St Paul, MN 55401
Meetings: First Monday of month. Location varies.
Annual Sale: Fall

Annual Dues: $15
Guest Fee: $3
Newsletter: Monthly

NEW JERSEY

Bead Society of New Jersey
P. O. Box 7465
Shrewsbury, NJ 07702
Eileen Cahill
Meetings: Second Monday of the month except August at 7 pm. Send SASE for meeting details. Meeting format varies.

Annual Dues: $20
Guest Fee: $3
Newsletter: Quarterly

New Mexico Bead Society **Annual Dues**: $15
P. O. Box 36824 **Guest Fee**: $1
Albuquerque, NM 87176-8624 **Newsletter**: Every other month
Meetings: Fourth Monday, 7 pm, Albuquerque Museum, 2000 Mountain Road, N.W. No July or December meeting.
Annual Sales: Spring and Fall Bead Bazaars, write for information.

NEW YORK
Bead Society of Greater New York **Annual Dues**: $25
P. O. Box 427 **Guest Fee**: $5
New York, NY 10116-0427 **Newsletter**: Monthly
Meetings: Last Wednesday of month September through June. Fashion Institute of Technology, 227 West 27th Street, New York City,

OHIO
Bead Society of Central Ohio **Phone**: 614-291-6565
249 King Avenue **Annual Dues**: $15
Columbus, OH 43201
Meetings: Third Monday of each month at 7:30 pm at Northminster Church, 203 King Avenue.

OREGON
Portland Bead Society **Phone**: 503-226-6482
P. O. Box 10611 **Annual Dues**: $10
Portland, OR 97210 **Guest Fee**: $2
Contact: Charlene Morrison **Newsletter** : Monthly
Meetings: Third Wednesday each month, 7 pm, Montgomery Park, 2701 NW Vaughn Street, Portland.
Annual Sale: Winter Bazaar and Summer Swap/Picnic.

PENNSYLVANIA
Brandywine Bead Society **Phone**: 215-793-2995
P. O. Box 860 **Annual Dues**: $15
Exton, PA 19341
Meetings: Call for information and location.

TEXAS
Austin Bead Society **Phone**: 512-452-5689
P. O. Box 656 **Annual Dues**: $15
Austin, TX 78767-0656 **Newsletter**: 10 times a year
Meetings: First Monday of the month at 6:30 pm at the Austin History Center, 810 Guadalupe, Austin.

San Antonio Bead Society
P. O. Box 700611
San Antonio, TX 78232-0611
Contact: Christine Saalbach
Phone: 210-494-7011
Annual Dues: $10
Newsletter: Quarterly
Meetings: Second Wednesday of the month, 7-8:30 pm, except for June through August. Location varies.

Panhandle Bead Association
P. O. Box 3747
Amarillo, TX 79116-3747
Contact: Beth Barringer
Phone: 806-383-4151
Annual Dues: $15
Newsletter: Quarterly
Meetings: Third Tuesday each month, 6:30 pm, call for location.

VIRGINIA

The Northern Virginia Bead Society **Phone:** 703-787-7486
P. O. Box 2150
Fairfax, VA 22031

WASHINGTON

The Northwest Bead Society
P.O. Box 15881
Seattle, WA 98115-0881
Phone: 206-325-2987
Annual Dues: $20 Individual
$30 Commercial
Meetings: Third Thursday every month September thru June, 7 pm, Art Center of Seattle, Pacific University, 3 West Cremona Street, Seattle.

Spokane Bead Society
P. O. Box 1208
Mead, WA 99021
Phone: 509-455-9315
Lee Ann Cogert, President
Meetings: Third Sunday every month except in the Summer.

WISCONSIN

Madison Bead Society
819 E. Johnson Street
Madison, WI 53703
Phone: 608-251-2583
Annual Dues: $10
Newsletter: Quarterly
Meetings: Second Tuesday or Wednesday monthly at 7:30 pm, call for information on place and presentation.

GREAT BRITAIN

Bead Society of Great Britain
Carole Morris
1 Casburn Lane, Burwell
Cambridgeshire CB5 0ED ENGLAND
Meetings: For information send two international reply coupons.

216 Bead Bazaars

These first three listings are for commercial shows. The remainder are sponsored by bead societies across the United States.

GEM FAIRE

P. O. Box 8329
Rancho Santa Fe, CA 92067
6060 Avenida Encinas
Carlsbad, CA 92009
Phone: 619-931-1410
FAX: 619-931-6808
Hours: All shows Fri 12-7 Sat 10-7 Sun 10-5
Owner: Allen Van Volkinburgh

Payment: Cks-MC-Visa-AE
Retail: Yes
Wholesale: Yes
Classes: At the Gem Faires

Gem Faire sponsors 47 annual faires across the US bringing together buyers, traders, designers and vendors from around the world to sell, trade and buy gems, beads, findings and books. Seminars and workshops at all faires. Also for sale at the faires are fossils, minerals and jewelry. **See the coupon section for one free admission to any show.**

THE WHOLE BEAD SHOW

3424 Silverado Trail
St. Helena, CA 94574
Phone: 707-963-2554
Fax: 707-963-1178
Hours: Mon-Fri 9-5
Owner: Ava Motherwell
Specialty: Bead shows. Call for exhibitor information

Payment: Cks-MC-Visa-AE
Retail: Yes
Wholesale: Yes

Ava sponsors bead shows across the United States. Call or write for the most current schedule. Her shows give you the opportunity to purchase beads directly from the beadmakers and traders and hot glass beadmaking demonstrations are given. You'll find thousands of beads, every size, shape and color at these shows.
May 95, Seattle, Washington
July 95, Newport Beach, California
September 95, San Francisco, California
October 95, Providence, Rhode Island
February 96, Tucson, Arizona.

THE BEAD RENAISSANCE

J & S Promotions, Ltd., Box 334
8007 West Colfax Avenue CS27
Lakewood, CO 80215-4090
Phone: 303-986-7566
Owner: Joan Johnson
Specialty: Bead shows

September 14 - 17, 1995
Free admission
10am - 6pm
Radisson Graystone Castle
Denver, Colorado

The Bead Renaissance, a wholesale and retail show will feature beads, beadmakers boutique, beadmaking demonstrations and bead jewelry. Free shuttle to and from the Denver Gem and Mineral Show.

BEAD SOCIETY BEAD BAZAARS

Always call or write to verify dates and location.

For free coupons for discounts on admission to some of these bazaars, or for the most current dates and new bazaars, please send a business size SASE.

CALIFORNIA

Northern California Bead Society
1650 Lower Grand Avenue
Piedmont, CA 94611
w/coupon
Location: Oakland Convention Center, 10th & Broadway
Vendor Information: Only members may exhibit.

May 6, 1995
9 am - 5 pm
Admission $3 - $2

The Bead Society (Los Angeles)
P. O. Box 241874
Los Angeles, CA 90024-9674
Location: Culver City Memorial Auditorium, Culver City.
Vendor Information: Only members may exhibit.

October 22, 1995

DISTRICT OF COLUMBIA

Bead Society of Greater Washington
P. O. Box 70036
Chevy Chase, MD 20813-0036
Third International Bead Conference.
See Conferences for complete information.

Nov. 17-19, 1995

IDAHO

Coeur d'Alene & Spokane Bead Societies
P. O. Box 5301
Coeur d'Alene, ID 83814-1955
Location: Intermountain Bead Bazaar, Eagle Lodge, Coeur d'Alene
Vendor Information: Send a large SASE for details.

July 2, 1995
10am - 8pm

ILLINOIS

Society of Glass Beadmakers
P. O. Box 895
Highland Park, IL 60035-0895
Location: Holiday Inn, Evanston, Illinois
This bazaar is part of the annual gathering, August 3-11, 1995.

August 6, 1995
10am - 3pm

Bead Society of Greater Chicago
P. O. Box 8103
Wilmette, IL 60091
Location: Mother Theodore Guerin High School, 8001 W. Belmont
Avenue. **Vendor Information:** Judith Schwab 708-699-7959

September 17, 1995
10am - 4pm
Admission $2

Chicago Midwest Bead Society
1020 Davis
Evanston, IL 60201 708-328-4040
Location: Evanston Holiday Inn, 1501 Sherman, Evanston, IL

November 12, 1995
11am - 5pm
Admission $3

MASSACHUSETTS

Beadesigner International
P. O. Box 503
Lincoln, MA 01773
Location: Armenian Cultural Center, 47 Nichols Ave., Watertown.
Vendor Information: Beadesigner members only.

October , 1995
Write for exact date
10am - 5pm

NEW MEXICO

New Mexico Bead Society
P. O. Box 36824
Albuquerque, NM 87176-9998
Vendor Information: Only New Mexico bead society members may
sell at May sale. **November sale** No restrictions on vendors.

November 1995
Write for exact dates
Free Admission

OREGON

Portland Bead Society
P. O. Box 10611
Portland, OR 97210
Location: Montgomery Park. **Vendors:** Members only .

Nov. 4 & 5, 1995
11am - 5pm
Admission $1

WASHINGTON

Northwest Bead Society
P. O. Box 15881
Seattle, WA 98115-0881
Location: Eckstein Middle School gym, 3003 NE 75th, Seattle
Vendor Information: Karen Murphy, Bazaar Chair (206) 632-7031

October 21-22, 1995
10am - 4 pm

Writing a bead book? We now offer consulting services for self-publishers. Please write for complete details.

For a list of books about marketing, selling and making money from your beadwork, please send a SASE.

Below is a partial list of the many books available about beads, beadwork, polymer clay and jewelry. If your local bead store cannot order these books for you, call the following places:

The Bead Museum, Prescott, Arizona (see Museums)
The Center for the Study of Beadwork, Oregon (see Associations)
Bead Society of Greater Washington (see Bead Societies)

BEAD-CRAFT
P. O. Box 4563
St. Paul, MN 55104
Phone: 612-645-1216
Hours: Call
Owner: Horace Goodhue
Payment: Cks
Retail: $10 one book
Wholesale: Call for discounts
Mail Order: Yes
Brochure: Yes
Specialty: *Indian Bead-Weaving Patterns* by Horace R. Goodhue

A manual written for beginning and advanced beaders. This 80 page book has 200 instructional illustrations and photographs of 47 beadwork pieces. It details the basic skills of bead-craft in its three main forms; freehand stringing, looming and embroidery using patterns the author learned through years of research with Native American people. After thirty years of teaching he has collected here his time-tested techniques for passing on to others a good foundation in beadcrafting.

JEANNETTE COOK & VICKI STAR
P. O. Box 60691
San Diego, CA 92166
Phone/Fax: 619-221-0328 or 633-1247
Hours: Mon-Fri 10-5
Payment: Cks
Retail: Yes
Wholesale: Yes
Mail Order: Yes
Specialty: How-to bead books and bead retreats.

Jeannette and Vicki conduct Bead Retreats. They also sell the work-books that go along with the retreats, *Beady Eyed Women's Guide To Exquisite Beadwork* - the series.

PRAIRIE CRAFT COMPANY

954 W. Washington Boulevard
Chicago, IL 60607
Phone: 312-421-6105
FAX: 312-633-0702
Hours: Mon-Fri 10-4
Owner: Donna Kato
Specialty: Publisher of instructional craft booklets

Payment: Cks
Retail: Yes
Wholesale: Call for discounts
Mail Order: Yes

They publish instructional materials with projects that are unique and challenging and inspire crafters to a new level of creativity designed on an intermediate level. The first set of books offer polymer clay projects designed by Donna Kato covering both Sculpey and Cernit.

SHERWOOD DESIGNS

P. O. Box 2106
Lakeside, CA 92040
Phone: 619-443-7982
FAX: 619-443-7841
Hours: Mon-Thurs 10-5
Owner: Jane Sherwood
Specialty: Beading books

Payment: Cks
Retail: Yes
Wholesale: 12 book minimum
Mail Order: Yes
Catalog: Yes

Sherwood Designs publishes and distributes a series of 10 how-to booklets. *Beaded Earrings*, $4.95; *Beaded Earrings-2 Advanced Designs*, $4.95; *Beaded Necklaces*, $5.95; *Embellishments* $4.95; *Pearls - Earrings and Necklaces* $4.95; *Glamour Earrings for Beginners* $4.95; *Beaded Barrettes and Bracelets* $4.95; *Ethnic Beading for Today* $5.95; *Fashion Jewelry Out of Fimo Clay* $5.95; and *Beaded Holiday Earrings* $5.95.

KATE DREW-WILKINSON/NOMAD PRESS

P. O. Box 1803
Bisbee, AZ 85603
Phone/Fax: 602-432-7117
Hours: Mon-Sun 9-5
Owner: Kate Drew-Wilkinson
Specialty: How-to books

Payment: Cks
Retail: Yes
Wholesale: $100 minimum
Mail Order: Yes

Basic Wire Work for Bead Jewelry is a comprehensive guide to working wire with beads, using only hand tools without soldering. The companion video of the same title demonstrates Kate's Closed Circuit techniques to create jewelry of superior strength and quality. *How to be Successful in the Bead Jewelry Business* is packed with information about many aspects of the bead business. It covers setting up a studio, exhibiting at shows, display, dealing with suppliers and different aspects of designing bead jewelry for sale.

How-To Books

Beads and Threads, by Diane Fitzgerald and Helen Banes published by Flower Valley Press shows new and inexpensive ways to create jewelry combining beads and threads. Beautifully illustrated and easy to follow directions.

Setting Stones with Beads by Barbara Ann Volk
This book clearly illustrates and gives easy-to-follow instructions on how to set stones on fabric or leather with beads. Available from the author, 41 Baltimore Street, Dept. TB, Glen Rock, PA 17327.

Creative Beaded Earrings, Volumes 1-4 by Veon Schunzel
Veon offers clearly written and easy-to-follow instructions on how to create beaded earrings.

Earring Designs by Sig: Book I by Sigrid Wynne-Evans
This book provides an answer to requests for new and different beading designs. Included are 46 new, original patterns for the Comanche stitch.

Those Bad Bad Beads by Virginia Blakelock and Carol Perrenoud
Included in this book are chapters on bead embroidery, beaded bags, loomwork, broad collars, peyote stitch and three African techniques. Universal Synergetics, Inc. , (see Mail Order listings)

Contemporary Loomed Beadwork by Therese Spears
This book teaches the loomwork process and offers step-by-step instructions, colored photographs and graphs of finished projects.

Beaded Clothing Techniques by Therese Spears
Included are sections on bead embroidery, use of the tambour shuttle for crochet chain beading, beaded fringe and bead edging. Promenade Publishing, P. O. Box 2092-BD, Boulder, CO 80306

Basic Wire Work for Bead Jewelry by Kate Drew-Wilkinson, $9.95. Learn closed circuit wire work with complete illustrated instructions on how to turn gold and silver wire and your favorite beads into prized jewelry.

Beads! Make your own unique jewellery by Stefany Tomalin
This book includes lots of illustrations and clear, easy-to-read instructions on how to make your own jewelry.

A PRIMER: the art of Native American Beadwork and the Video - *A Primer: Sewn Beadwork & Blanket Border Stitch* by Z. Susanne Aikman. A good basic book and video for learning Indian-style beadwork techniques. Included are net patterns, loomwork, peyote stitch, Comanche weave and beaded edgings. Morning Flower Press, Denver, CO.

Embroidery With Beads by Angela Thompson published by Lacis, Berkeley, CA. This book covers the subject of bead embroidery in rich, lavish detail and discusses the history and uses of bead embroidery and the types of beads which may be stitched to cloth. Included are many pages of various techniques.

Beading with Seed Beads, Gem Stones & Cabochons by Sadie Starr, $24.95 Easy step-by-step instructions so you can create your own unique, handcrafted wearable art. Included are many patterns, illustrations and color photos.

Ethnic Beads and Beadwork

Beads and Beadwork of West and Central Africa by Margret Carey This book covers the area from Senegal to Zaire, and the Sahara to Southern Angola and Zaire. Included are photos of sample cards used in trade, a discussion of bead types including lengthy descriptions of beadmaking in Africa, and much more.

Ethnic Jewelry John Mack (Ed.) Harry N. Abrams, Inc., New York. Experts from around the world explain how such jewelry has been made and worn, the relationship of the materials to the culture and how the manufacturing techniques survived for centuries.

Native American Beads and Beadwork

Trade Ornament Usage Among the Native Peoples of Canada: A Source Book by Karlis Karklins. This study describes in chronological order how the various trade ornaments (glass beads, wampum, etc.) were used from initial contact to circa 1900 by representative tribes of the seven major indigenous groups of Canada.

Beads: Their Use by Upper Great Lakes Indians, Gordon L. Olson, Project Director. Four scholarly essays are followed by 40 pages of black and white photographs of the exhibition for which this book was the catalog.

History, Reference

The New Beadwork by Kathlyn Moss and Alice Scherer
The first book ever published on the art of contemporary beadwork. Published by Harry N. Abrams, Inc., available for $29.95 plus $2 shipping from The Center for the Study of Beadwork. **Discount coupon for this book in the back of the Directory.** This bellwether book brings national exposure to a truly "new" art form. Featured works in *The New Beadwork* range from Steve Wofford's incredibly detailed baskets (1" or less), to Jeanne Leffingwell's "Sky Curtain," a 30x30x30' architectural piece using over five million seed beads.

Speaking With Beads, Zulu Arts from Southern Africa by Jean Morris, Thames and Hudson, $19.95. This beautifully photographed book with 152 color illustrations is a must have for all bead collectors. This book shows jewelry, ornamental headdresses, capes, aprons, beaded panels and other decorative forms.

Beads of The World by Peter Francis, Jr., Schiffer Publishing, $19.95. A collector's guide with price reference. The author brings years of his research to this book in the broadest reference available to date. Bead types are discussed and traced to their origins.

Baubles, Buttons and Beads: The Heritage of Bohemia by Sibylle Jargstorf, Schiffer Publishing $29.95. This book exposes the jewelers, craftsmanship and history of Bohemia. Gorgeous color photos show the artistry, its most significant designers and manufacturers and their contributions to the art of jewelry, button and beadmaking.

The History of Beads (from 30,000 B.C. to the Present) by Lois Sherr Dubin, available from the Center for the Study of Beadwork, $65 & $3 shipping. The author has brought together the history of beads and updated the previous books on the subject of beads in stunningly beautiful style. This is the most comprehensive book on the history of beads.

Glass in Jewelry : Hidden Artistry in Glass by Sibylle Jargstorf, Schiffer Publishing. A showcase of the use of European made glass beads in jewelry.

A Bead Primer by Elizabeth Harris. Published by The Bead Museum. Describes several methods of bead-making, both ancient and modern.

Listed below are some of the books available from the Center for Bead Research. The CBR has produced a series of monographs on topics such as Venetian and Czech beads, Third World Beadmakers, and two books on bead terms and materials that are necessary to anyone truly interested in bead history. For a complete catalog of books write to: 4 Essex Street, Lake Placid, NY 12946.

A Dictionary of Bead Terms and Types
The Glass Trade Beads of Europe: Their Manufacture, Their History, and Their Identification
Beads and the Discovery of the New World
Chinese Glass Beads: A Review of the Evidence
Heirloom and Ethnographically Collected Beads In Southeast Asia ´

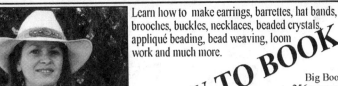

POLYMER CLAY BOOKS

Creative Clay Jewelry, Designs to Make from Polymer Clay , Leslie Dierks, Lark Books, Asheville, NC, $18.95.
This books shows you how to handle polymer clay, which tools to use and how to create hundreds of beautiful designs. Clear, step-by-step instructions and dozens of color illustrations. A fun book to have.

The New Clay: Techniques and Approaches To Jewelry Making by Nan Roche, Flower Valley Press, $22.95. Everything you need to know to be successful in working with polymer clay is covered clearly in this book. Easy to follow diagrams and over 100 color photographs.

225 Books

BEADWORK VIDEOS

Beadweaving Peyote Stitch by Carol Perrenoud, 87 minutes. This video teaches you how to follow peyote stitch design graphs and tips on how to make a peyote stitch graph of your own design for future projects. You'll also create your own beaded pouch necklace.

Techniques of Beading Earrings with Deon DeLange, 76 minutes. Deon teaches you how to create earrings in all of the most popular styles.

Bead Woven Necklaces- Loom Beading Techniques by Virginia Blakelock, 82 minutes, $39.95. Step-by-step construction of a loomwork necklace. You'll learn basic weaving and finishing and all about beads and other supplies. Available from Universal Synergetics (see Oregon listings)

GLASS BEADMAKING VIDEOS

IMPORTANT - Do not use videos only to learn glass beadmaking. There are many things including safety features of working with hot glass that cannot be learned from a video. Use these videos in conjunction with a personal hands on class. Many of the beadmakers listed in the Directory teach classes.

TIP: "Safety is the most important part of glass beadmaking. Before you begin making glass beads talk with a professional about the proper way to set up your workshop. You might also want to consult your welding supplier or oxygen supplier, each of whom can give you the proper safety tips for working with the equipment you buy from them." Kim Osibin, Beadmaker and teacher.

Beadmaking, by Michael Max, 60 minutes, available from Modern Alchemy (see Glass Beadmakers listings). Working with Moretti glass Michael clearly demonstrates some basic bead shapes, decorative techniques, component parts and shows the basic tools needed. He goes over annealing and teaches how to read the nature of the glass.

Lewis Wilson has a series of videos covering many glass beadmaking techniques. Lewis has been working with glass for over 20 years and introduces the viewer to many techniques and gives precise and detailed descriptions of each step demonstrated. To order the videos below, by Lewis Wilson, and to get information on his latest videos, see the listing for Crystal Myths under Glass Beadmakers.

Lampworking, Advanced Beads, Bracelets, Marbles covers advanced beadmaking techniques such as lattacino, pulled goldstone stringer, moretti dichroic, Phoenician face beads and amphora bottles. This four hour video is in two parts.

Animal Beads and Glass Candies, 111 minutes, shows the construction of 12 beads and techniques for making animal beads and glass candies.

CLASSES

The following bead stores offer classes. Look in the state listings for the address and phone number. Each bead store offers so many unusual classes that it would be impossible to list each class. The variety of classes ranges from basic knotting, beaded embroidery, beaded watchbands, to how-to make your own findings. Each store has its own selection of great teacher s and unique classes. Try several different stores to get the best variety of classes and make sure to attend classes while travelling. Call the stores for class schedules and mention *The Bead Directory*.

Alaska
Bead Heaven - Anchorage
Beads & Things - Fairbanks
Spirit Beads - Juneau

Arizona
Bead Connection - Tucson
Bead It! - Prescott
The Bead Source - Tucson
Beads & Adornables - Glendale
Beadbox - Scottsdale
Be-Jeweled - Phoeniz
Cocopah - Sedona
Double Joy - Scottsdale
Dream Weaver - Bisbee
Jac Jan - Sedona
Piney Hollow - Tucson
Scottsdale Bead - Scottsdale
Sedona Beads - Sedona
Shooting Starr - Camp Verde
Tombstone Bead - Tombstone

California
Artistry With Beads - Burbank
Ascona Beads - Santa Monica
Barbettas Beads - Sacramento
Baubles & Beads - Berkeley
Bead Bazaar - Pleasanton
Bead Box - Los Angeles
Bead Bungalow - Redding
The Bead Fetish - San Rafael
The Bead Gallery - Red Bluff

California cont.'d
Bead Gallery-Manhattan Beach
Bead Ranch - Sunnyvale
Bead Shack - Santa Rosa
The Bead Shop - Laguna Beach
The Bead Shop - Palo Alto
The Bead Shop - Los Altos
The Bead Shop - San Jose
The Bead Store - Palm Desert
The Beaded Bear - San Jose
The Beaded Nomad - Napa
Beads, Baskets - Bakersfield
Beads Beads - Orange
Beads Beads - Corona
Beads By The Bay - Morro Bay
Beads and More - Encinitas
Beads and More - San Diego
Beads of Marin - Mill Valley
Beads N' Things - Seal Beach
Beads Unique - Bakersfield
Beadz - Fresno
Bell Tower Beads - Placerville
Black Sheep - Encinitas
Broadway Bead - Walnut Creek
Chester Bead - Mill Valley
Creative Expressions-Palm Sprs
Cynabar Designs - Reseda
El Dorado - San Francisco
Farrin O'Connor - Pasadena
Frugal's Beads - Culver City
Full Moon Beads - Novato
Garden of Beadin - Redway

California cont.'d

Gargoyle - San Francisco
Gee Jay's - ANtioch
Gotsie's - Huntington Beach
Heart Bead - Arcata
Heart Beads - Castro Valley
JBJ Originlas - Berkeley
Katherine's - Grand Terrace
Legandary Beads - Petaluma
Magical Trinket - San Francisco
Orb Weaver - Oakland
Oskadusa - Solana Beach
Palo Pacifica - Pacific Grove
Peninsula Bead - San Jose
The Place To Bead - San Ramon
The Shepherdess - San Diego
Spotted Pony - San Pablo
String Bead - Chico
Wild Thing's - Livermore

Colorado

Beads & Beyond - Durango
Int'l Beadtrader - Englewood
Morning Flower - Denver
Morning Light - Paonia
Pearls & Jewels - Denver
Promenade's - Boulder
Skyloom Fibres - Denver

Connecticut

Beadworks - South Norwalk

Delaware

Mad Cat - Wilmington

District of Columbia

Beadazzled - D.C.

Florida

The Bead String - Jacksonville
Beads F.O.B. - Sarasota
Chevron Trading - Tallahassee
Crystal Creations - W. Palm Bch
D. J. Whimsy - Sarasota
Gifts of Avalon - Gainesville

Florida cont.'d

Poppa Burke's - Fernandina Bch
Worldbeads - Miami
Worldbeads - Plantation
Worldbeads - Aventura

Georgia

The Bead Shoppe - Morganton

Hawaii

Dacs Beads - Honolulu
Fantasy Works - Haiku, Maui

Idaho

Mountain Man - Wallace
7 Trumpets - Coeur d'Alene
Zizzyzaza - Coeur d'Alene

Illinois

Bead In Hand - Oak Park
Bead It! - Chicago
The Bead Lady - Champaign
Beadazzled - Evanton
The Beadhive - Geneva
Bodacious Beads - Des Plaines
Caravan Beads - Chicago
Int'l Beadtrader - Glen Ellyn
Int'l Beadtrader - Park Ridge
Originals - Evanston

Indiana

Bead Workshop - South Bend
Just Beads - Bargersville

Kansas

Int'l Beadtrader - Lawrence
Int'l Beadtrader - Wichita

Maine

Caravan Beads - Portland

Maryland

Accents - Bethesda
Beadazzled - Baltimore
Bead It! - Towson

Maryland cont.'d
Beadworks - Baltimore
Hurricane - Baltimore

Massachusetts
Bead Connection - Wellesley
Beads Etc. - Arlington
Beadworks - Cambridge
Beadworks - Boston
Crystal Blue - Watertown
The Pear Tree - Brookline
The Stoneworks - Dunstable
Wandering Bull - Attleboro

Michigan
Birmingham Bead - Birmingham
Currie Beads - St. Joseph

Minnesota
Bead It! - Bloomington
Beautiful Beads - Minneapolis
Bijoux - Roseville
Bobby Bead - Minneapolis
Cosecha - Wayzata
Creative Fibers - Minneapolis

Missouri
Bead It! - St. Louis
Int'l Beadtrader - Kansas City
Terranean Designs - Springfield
Veon Creations - Desoto
White Heart - St. Louis
Zuma Beach - St. Louis

Montana
Powder Horn - Kalispell

Nebraska
Int'l Beadtrader - Lincoln

Nevada
Beauty & Beads - Carson City
Love-R-Beads - Las Vegas

New Hampshire
Beady Eye - Keene
Caravan Beads - North Conway
Fiber Studio - Henniker
Mad As A Hatter - Exeter
Tracey's - North Hampton

New Jersey
Bead Stampede - Bogota
Beads Glorious! - Tenafly
Riverstone - Medham

New Mexico
All Strung Out - Taos
Melanie - Albuquerque
Southwest - Albuquerque
Stone Mountain - Albuquerque

New York
Accents - Buffalo
Bead Store Cafe - Ithaca
Bead Street - Port Jefferson
Kuma - Glenville

North Carolina
Night Bead - Iron Station
Original Ornament - Chapel Hill

Ohio
Bead Paradise - Oberlin
Byzantium - Columbus
Isle of Beads - Cleveland Heights

Oklahoma
Int'l Beadtrader - Tulsa
Int'l Beadtrader - Norman

Oregon
Adornments - Medford
Bead Garden - Salem
Bead Merchant - Grants Pass
Bead Street - Portland
Bead Studio - Ashland
Dava Bead - Portland

Oregon con't.
Deon's Originale - Waldport
Looking Glass - Ashland
Multnomah - Portland
Portland Bead - Portland
Worldbeads - Portland

Pennsylvania
Barbara Ann Volk - Glen Rock

South Carolina
One By One - Greenville

South Dakota
Sioux Trading Post - Rapid City

Texas
Bead It! - El Paso
Las Canadas - Amarillo
Mila's - Austin
Worldbeads - Houston

Virginia
Bead Garden - Fredericksburg
Bead Shop - Newport News
Beads & Rocks - Virginia Beach
Beadazzled - McLean
Star's - Vienna

Washington
Bead Bazaar - Bellingham
Bead Boppers - Puyallup
Bead Factory - Seattle
Bead Store - Auburn
Beads & Beyond - Bellevue
Beads Indeed! - Seattle
Island Beads - Seattle
Northwest Passage - Bremerton
Temptations - North Bend

Wisconsin
Blue Bead - Madison
Knot Just Beads - West Allis
Lulu's - Appleton

Wisconsin con't.
Tropic Jewel - Madison
Turtle Island - Baraboo

Glass Beadmaking Classes

Most of these teachers travel
across the United States to teach.

Arrow Springs - California
Holland & Sage - Arkansas
Boutz Family - Tennessee
Crystal Myths - New Mexico
Fancy's - Arizona
Fineline Studios - Colorado
Kate Fowle - District of Columbia
Gaea Glassworks - California
Gardens of Glass - California
Gossamer Glass - Washington
Inner Light - California
Ginger Kelly - Washington
Kristina Logan - New Hampshire
Kris Peterson - Clarkston
Modern Alchemy - Washington
Potek Studio - Wisconsin
Don Schneider - Michigan
Heather Trimlett - California
Victoria Alexis - California
Pati Walton - Colorado

Beadmaking Suppliers offering classes:
Bead Supplies Intl - Maryland
Northwest Art - Washington
Wale Apparatus - Pennsylvania

Paper Beadmaking Classes
Judith Content - California

Polymer Beadmaking Classes
Mirabai Arts - New Hampshire
More Beads - Virginia
Nesting Heart - Washington

BEAD CONFERENCES

BEADS Through the Eye of the Collector.
Third International Bead Conference sponsored by the Bead Society of Greater Washington.

November 17-19, 1995, Washington D.C.
The proceeds of the conference will be devoted to moving The Bead Museum from Arizona and establishing it in Washington, DC as an enduring institution dedicated to beads and personal adornments from ancient, ethnic and contemporary cultures.

Keynote Speaker, Robert K. Liu, Co-editor of Ornament. Guest of Honor, Gabrielle Liese, Director of The Bead Museum.

For complete information and registration information: Third International Bead Conference, P. O. Box 2666-0666, Fairfax VA 22031. FAX: 703-273-2864, Phone: 410-987-1884 for recorded information.

Bead Expo '96. Stone Beads: From the Heart of the Earth.

Peter Francis, Jr., Symposium Director
March 6-12, 1996, San Antonio, Texas

Bead Expo is produced by the Center for Bead Research and Recursos de Santa Fe in cooperation with the San Antonio and Austin Bead Societies.

In addition to the Bazaar and Symposium, Bead Expo features exhibits, workshops, seminars and city-wide events. **For information contact:** Recursos de Santa Fe, 826 Camino del Monte Rey #A3, Santa Fe, NM 87505. Phone: 505-982-9301. FAX: 505-989-8608

Third

International

BEAD CONFERENCE

November 17, 18 & 19, 1995
Washington DC

BEADS:
THROUGH THE EYE
OF THE COLLECTOR

Three-day Symposium
International Bead Bazaar
Workshops & Panel Discussions
Designer Showcase

Third International Bead Conference
PO BOX 2666-0666, FAIRFAX VA 22031
410 987-1884   Fax: 703 273-2864

sponsored by
The Bead Society of Greater Washington

MAGAZINES/NEWSLETTERS

Your best source for current information on beads is to subscribe to the newsletters written by the Center for the Study of Beadwork, the Society of Bead Researchers, and the Center for Bead Research (see Associations for further information). *Ornament* magazine is your best source for articles on beads and jewelry. The other magazines and newsletters listed below sometimes feature stories on beads.

Fiberworks Publications
Bobbi A. McRae
P. O. Box 49770-T
Austin, TX 78765-9770
Bobbi publishes a quarterly newsletter on the fiber arts and *The New Fiberworks Sourcebook*.

Jewelry Crafts
4880 Market Street, Dept. TBD
Ventura, CA 93003
805-644-3824
A bi-monthly magazine featuring articles on how-to make and sell jewelry.

Ornament
P. O. Box 2349-BD
San Marcos, CA 92079-2349
800-888-8950
A beautifully illustrated magazine with articles on beads, beadwork and other personal adornment.

PieceWork
Contact: Barbara Liebler, Advertising Salesperson
201 East Fourth Street - Dept. TBD
Loveland, CO 80537
303-669-7672
PieceWork is a wonderful magazine on handwork that will sometimes feature articles on beadwork.

Whispering Wind
8009 Wales Street-B
New Orleans, LA 70126
504-246-3742
A magazine devoted to the American Indian, past and present.

MUSEUMS

There is only one Bead Museum in the United States currently located in Prescott, Arizona. Plans are underway to move The Bead Museum to Washington, D.C. If you or your Bead Society can help in any way with the fundraising efforts, contact the museum.

Craft and folk art museums occasionally have exhibits of beadwork. Anthropology museums are a good place to find ethnic bead collections and *Ornament* magazine is a good source for information on bead exhibits.

The Bead Museum
140 South Montezuma, Prescott, AZ 86303 - 602-445-2431

The Bead Museum is a non-profit museum with both permanent, temporary and traveling exhibits of beads and adornments from all parts of the world and almost all periods of history. The museum store sells books on beads and related subjects and selections of unusual and hard-to-find beads. A mail order catalog is available for $2 to non-members. There is no catalog for the beads since they change frequently. Members receive a 20% discount on the books, a free subscription to the Bead Museum Quarterly, and free visits to the museum. Hours: Mon-Sat 9:30 - 4:30, open Sunday by appointment. Closed on certain holidays.

Bead Types: A- All kinds O- Old E- Ethnic N- New U - Unique	Page No.	Beads	Tools	Find- ings	Cus- tom Work	Bks	Con- sign- ment
ALASKA							
The Bead Gallery	1	A	x	x	x		
Bead Heaven	1	A	x	x	x		
Beads And Things	1	A-E	x	x			
Killer Beads	2	O-E-U			x		
Spirit Beads	2	A	x	x		x	
ARIZONA							
The Bead Connection	2	A	x	x	x		
Bead It!	2	A		x		x	x
Bead Source	3	A					
Beads & Adornables	3	A	x	x		x	
Beads Galore	4	A	x	x		x	
Beadbox, Inc.	4	A	x	x		x	
Beaucoup Beads Limited	4	O-N	Czech glass				
Be-Jeweled By Mary	5	A		x	x		
Black Star Trading Co.	5	E-U					
Bovis Bead Co	5	A-U					
Cocopah Jewelry Co.	6	E-O-U	x	x	x		
The Copper Coyote	6	N-O	Japanese seed beads				
Double Joy Beads	6	A		x	x		
Dream Weaver Beads	7	A	x	x	x	x	
Hardies	7	A	x	x		x	
JacJan Beads, Etc.	7	A		x			
Kiva Arts	8	Huichol Indian beadwork					
Piney Hollow	8	A	x	x	x	x	
Scottsdale Bead Supply	8	A		x		x	
Sedona Beads	9	A	x	x	x	x	
Shooting Starr Gallery	9	A		x		x	
Tombstone Beads Co.	9	O-E-U	x	x	x	x	
Uptown Tribal	10	U		x	x	x	
Venetian Traders	10	O-E	Venetian glass beads				
Wishbone's Trading Post	10	O-E-U		x			
ARKANSAS							
Southwestern Beads	11	O-E-U			x		
CALIFORNIA							
Juliet Anderson	13	E-N					
Artistry With Beads	13	A	x	x	x	x	
Ascona Beads	13	A	x	x	x		
Azumane	14	E-U	Rare beads				
Barbetta's Beads	14	A	x	x	x	x	
Baubles & Beads	14	A	x	x	x	x	
Bead Bazaar	15	A	x	x	x	x	

Bead Types: A- All kinds O- Old E- Ethnic N- New U - Unique	Page No.	Beads	Tools	Findings	Custom Work	Bks	Consignment
California (Con't)							
The Bead Boutique	15	A	x	x			
Bead Box	16	A	x	x	x	x	
Bead Bungalow	16	A	x	x	x		
The Bead Fetish	16	A	x	x	x	x	
Bead Gallery /Red Bluff	17	A	x	x			
Bead Gallery	17	A	x		x		
Bead It	18	A	x	x	x	x	
Bead Mania	18	A	x	x		x	
Bead Ranch	18	N-E-U	x	x	x	x	x
The Bead Shack	19	A	x	x			
Bead Shop/Laguna Bch	19	A	x	x	x		
The Bead Shop/Palo Alto	19	A	x	x	x	x	
The Bead Shop/Los Altos	20	A	x	x	x	x	x
The Bead Shop/San Jose	20	A	x	x	x	x	x
Bead Station	21	A		x	x		
Bead Station	21	A		x	x		
The Bead Store	21	A	x	x	x		
Bead Werk	22	A	x	x	x	x	
The Beaded Bear	22	Designer/Teacher/How-To Books					
The Beaded Nomad	23	A	x	x	x	x	
The Beadman	23	A	x	x	x	x	
Beads	23	A	x	x	x	x	
Beads, Baskets Memories	24	A		x	x	x	
Beads Beads	25	A	x	x	x	x	
Beads Beads	26	A	x	x	x .	x	
Beads By The Bay	26	A	x	x	x	x	
Beads Etc.	26	A	x	x	x	x	
Beads and More	27	A	x	x	x	x	
Beads Of Marin	27	A		x	x		
Beads & Ornaments	28	E-U	Designer/glass beadmaker				
Beads N' Things	29	A	x	x	x	x	
Beads To You	29	A	x	x		x	
Beads Unique	29	A	x	x	x	x	
Beadz	29	A	x	x	x	x	
Bell Tower Beads Plus	31	A	x	x	x	x	
Bijoux Fous	31	N-U	Designer			x	
The Black Beads	31	A	x	x		x	
The Black Sheep	32	E-U		x		x	
Broadway Bead	32	A	x	x	x	x	
Burley's Crafts	32	A	x			x	x	
Bwanacon	33	E	African goods				

Bead Types: A- All kinds / O- Old E- Ethnic / N- New U - Unique	Page No.	Beads	Tools	Find-ings	Cus-tom Work	Bks	Con-sign-ment
California (Con't)							
Chester Bead	33	A	x	x		x	
Chico Bead	33	A	x	x	x	x	
Creative Expressions	34						
Cynabar Designs	34	A	x	x	x		
Due South Imports	34	E	Guatemalan handicrafts				
Eagle Beads	35	O-E-U		x		x	
El Dorado	35	A	x	x			
Glenn Erso	36	E-N	Sterling silver beads & clasps				
Expedition	38	A	x	x			
Fantasy Beads	38	A	x	x	x	x	
Farrin O'Connor	38	A	x	x	x	x	x
The Fashion Company	40						
Fogel's	40	O-U	Antique beads				
The Folk Tree Collection	40						
Frugal's Beads	42						
Full Moon Beads	42						
Garden of Beadin'	42	A	x	x	x	x	
Gargoyle Beads	43						
Gee Jay's U Name It	43						
General Bead	43	A	x	x		x	
Global Beads	44						
Gotsie's	45	A	x	x	x	x	
Gypsy Wind Bead & Trim	45	A	x	x		x	
Heart Bead/Arcata	45	A	x	x	x	x	
Heart Beads/Castro Valley	46	A	x	x	x	x	x
Himalayan Trading Co.	47	E	Tibetan beads and ornaments				
House of Beads	47	A	x	x	x	x	
Int'l Bead & Jewelry	47	A	x	Beads from Israel			
JBJ Originals	48	N					
Kahn-Fagan	48	A-O-U					
Katherine's Beads	48						
Lacis	49	N-O-U					
Legendary Beads	49	A-E-U	x	x		x	
The Magical Trinket	50	A-E-U	x	x	x	x	
The Name Game	50	N	Wooden letter & symbol beads				
Native Star Crafts	50		Beadcraft kits				
Rita Okrent	51	O-E-U	Designer				
Orb Weaver	52	A	x	x	x	x	
Oskadusa	52	A	x	x	x	x	x
Out On A Whim	53	A	x	x			
Palo Pacifica	53	A	x	x	x	x	

Bead Types: A- All kinds O- Old E- Ethnic N- New U - Unique	Page No.	Beads	Tools	Find-ings	Cus-tom Work	Bks	Con-sign-ment
California (Con't)							
Peninsula Bead & Supply	53	A	x	x		x	
Perl House	54	E-N-U	x	x			
Peruvian Bead Co.	54	A	x	x		x	
The Place To Bead	54	A	x	x	x	x	
Reedtz Beads	55	A	x	x		x	
Ritual Adornments	55						
The Sherpherdess	56	A-U		Classes			
Spotted Pony	57		Designer & How-to Books				
String Bead	57						
Sweets	57	A	x	x			
U Bead It	57	A	x	x			
Wild Thing's	58	A	x	x	x	x	x
Yone	58	A		x			
COLORADO							
Amallama	60	E-U	x	x	x	x	
Beads and Beyond	60	A	x	x			
Int'l Beadtrader	61	A	x	x	x	x	
Morning Flower Press	61	E			x	x	
Morning Light Emporium	62	A			x		
One Of A Kind	62	E-U		x			
Ornamental Resources	62	A	x	x		x	
Pearls & Jewels Bead Shop	63	A	x	x	x	x	
Promenade's Le Bead	63	A	x	x	x	x	
Silver & Beads	63	A	x	x		x	
Skyloom Fibres	64	A	x	x	x		
Worldbeads	64	A	x	x	x	x	
CONNECTICUT							
Beadazzled	64	A	x	x	x	x	
Beadworks	65	A	x	x		x	
Watch Us	66	Watch findings, parts and watch heads					
DELAWARE							
Mad Cat	67	A	x	x	x	x	
DISTRICT OF COLUMBIA							
Beadazzled	67	A	x	x			
Harmattan Arts	68	E-U	African arts				
FLORIDA							
Bead Gypsies	68	A					
The Bead String	68	A	x	x	x	x	
Beads F.O.B.	69	A	x	x	x		
Chevron	69	A-E-U	x	x	x	x	
Crystal Creations	70	A	x	x			

Bead Types: A- All kinds O- Old E- Ethnic N- New U - Unique	Page No.	Beads	Tools	Find-ings	Cus-tom Work	Bks	Con-sign-ment
Florida cont.d							
D.J. Whimsy!	70	A	x	x	x	x	
Gifts of Avalon	71	A	x	x	x		
Poppa Burke's	71	A-E	x	x			
Worldbeads	71	A	x	x			
Worldbeads	72	A	x	x			
GEORGIA							
Bead Shoppe	73	A	x	x	x		
Beadazzles	73	A	x	x	x		
Dal Crafts	73	Bead tray and storage for beads					
HAWAII							
A Little Craft	74	A	x	x			
DACS Beads	74	A	x	x	x		
Fantasy Works	75	A	x	x	x		
IDAHO							
Mountain Main	76	A-U	x	x			
7 Trumpets	76	A	x	x	x	x	
Zizzyzaza	76	A	x	x	x		
ILLINOIS							
Bead In Hand	77	A	x	x			
Bead It!	77	A	x	x	x		
Bead Lady	78	E-U	x	x	x		
Beadazzled	78	A	x	x	x	x	x
The Beadhive	78	A	x	x			
Bodacious Beads	79	A	x	x			
Caravan Beads	79	A	x	x	x	x	x
DA Beads	79	E-U					
Int'l Beadtrader	80	A	x	x	x		
Int'l Beadtrader	81	A	x	x	x		
Originals	81	E-U-N	x	x	x	x	x
Queen Beads	81	Japanese seed beads					
INDIANA							
Bead Workshop	82	A	x	x	x	x	
Just Beads	82	A	x	x	x	x	
IOWA							
Unique Creations	82	A	x	x	x		
KANSAS							
Int'l Beadtrader	83	A	x	x			
MAINE							
Beadin' Path	85	A	x	x			
Caravan Beads	85	A	x	x			

Bead Types: A- All kinds O- Old E- Ethnic N- New U - Unique	Page No.	Beads	Tools	Findings	Custom Work	Bks	Consignment
MARYLAND							
Accents	86	A	x	x	x	x	x
Beadazzled	86	A	x	x	x	x	x
Beadecked	87	A	x	x			
Bead It!	87	A	x	x		x	
Beadworks	87	A	x	x		x	
Fantasy Beads	87	A	x	x			
Hurricane	88	A	x	x	x	x	
Marvin Schwab	88	A					
MASSACHUSETTS							
Bead Connection Too	89	A	x	x		x	x
Beadniks	89	A	x	x	x	x	x
Beads Etc.	90	A	x	x		x	
Beadworks	90	A	x	x	x		
Crystal Blue	91	A	x	x		x	
Pear Tree	91	A	x	x	x	x	
Singaraja	91	E-U					
Stoneworks	92	N-U					
Tavros Leather	93	Leather goods					
Wandering Bull	93	E-U	Native American				
MICHIGAN							
Beadworks	94	A	x	x	x	x	x
Birmingham Bead Store	94	A	x	x	x	x	
Currie Beads	95	A	x	x		x	
Michigan Lapidary Co.	95	A	x	x			
Noc Bay Trading Co.	95	E-U	x	x	x		
MINNESOTA							
Bead It!	96	A	x	x		x	
Beautiful Beads	96	A	x	x	x	x	
The Bead Monkey	97						
Bijoux Bead	97	A	x	x	x	x	
Bobby Bead	97	A	x	x	x	x	
Creative Fibers	98						
Cosecha Designs	98	A	x	x	x	x	
MISSOURI							
B & J Rock Shop	98	A	x	x		x	
Bead It!	99						
Int'l Beadtrader	99	A	x	x			
Terranean Designs	99						
Veon Creations	100	A	How-To books				
White Heart Trading Post	100						
Zuma Beach Bead Co.	202	A	x	x	x		x

Bead Types: A- All kinds O- Old E- Ethnic N- New U - Unique	Page No.	Beads	Tools	Find-ings	Cus-tom Work	Bks	Con-sign-ment
MONTANA							
Old Bozeman Beads	102	E-U	x	x		x	
Four Winds Trading Post	101	E-U	x	x	x		
Powder Horn Trading Pst	102	E-U	x	x		x	
NEBRASKA							
Int'l Beadtrader	102	A	x	x	x		
NEVADA							
Beads Plus	103	A	x	x	x		
Beauty & The Beads	103	N-E-U		x		x	
Love-R-Beads	103	A	x	x	x		
Sugarpine Trading Co.	104	E-U					
Supplies 4 Less	104	A	Craft supplies				
Sweetwater Trading Co.	104	O-E-U					
NEW HAMPSHIRE							
The Beady Eye	105	A	x	x			
Caravan Beads	105	A	x	x	x	x	
The Fiber Studio	105	U					
Mad As A Hatter	106	Bead Kits					
Overseas Mining	106	N-U See the color insert					
Tracey's	106	A	x	x	x		
NEW JERSEY							
The Bead Stampede	107	A	x	x	x	x	
Beads Glorious!	107	A		x	x	x	
Riverstone	107	A	x	x	x		
The Sojourner	108	A	x	x	x		
NEW MEXICO							
All Strung Out	108	A	x	x	x		
Anahita Gallery	108	E	Jewelry & Textiles				
The Bead Caravan	109	E-U		x			
Bead World Inc.	109	A	x	x			
Beauty and the Beads	109	A	x	x	x	x	
Craft Enterprises	110	A	x	x			
Indian Jewelers Supply	110	N-E-U	Metal beads				
Max Hand Leather Goods	111		Leather				
Melanie Collection	111	A	x	x	x	x	
Mythmakers	112	Sterling and bronze components					
Nina Designs	113	E-N-U	Sterling silver beads				
Sioux Trading Post	113	Native American					
Southwest America	113	A	x	x	x	x	x
Stone Mountain Bead	114	A	x	x	x	x	
Stone Mountain Trading	114	E-U					
Winona Trading Post	115	A	x	x		x	

Bead Types: A- All kinds O- Old E- Ethnic N- New U - Unique	Page No.	Beads	Tools	Find-ings	Cus-tom Work	Bks	Con-sign-ment
Worldly Goods	116	A		x	x		
NEW YORK							
Accents Bead Shop	116	A	x	x	x		
Bead House	116	A	x	x	x		
Bead Store Cafe	117	A	x	x	x	x	
Bead Street, Ltd.	117	A	x	x	x		
Beads of Paradise	117	E-U African beads and textiles					
Beyond Beadery	119	A Native American					
Helby Import Co.	119	Wholesale to bead stores only					
Kuma Beads	119	A	x	x	x	x	
Myron Toback Inc.	121	A	x	x			
Margola Import Corp.	120	A	x	x			
York Novelty Import Co.	122	A					
NORTH CAROLINA							
Bead Struk	122	A	x	x	x	x	
Night Bead Beadworks	122	Seed beads					
The Original Ornament	123	A	x	x	x	x	
The Roddy Gallery	123	E-U				x	
The Source Rock Shop	124	A	x	x	x		
OHIO							
A2Z Craft Supply	124	A	x	x			
Beads & Things	124	A	x	x	x		
Bead Paradise	125	A	x	x	x	x	
Byzantium	125	A	x	x	x	x	x
Discount Bead House	125	A					
Granger City Beads	126	E-U					
Isle of Beads	126	A	x	x	x	x	x
OKLAHOMA							
Int'l Beadtrader	127	A	x	x	x	x	
OREGON							
Adornments	127	A	x	x	x	x	x
Africa John's	128	Custom made beads					
Baker Bay Bead Co.	128	A	x	x			
The Bead Garden	129	A	x	x			
The Bead Merchant	129	A	x	x	x	x	x
A Bead Source	130	A	x	x	x	x	x
Bead Street	130	A	x	x	x	x	x
The Bead Studio	131	A	x	x	x	x	x
C&GG Crafts	131	A	Craft supplies				
Dava Bead & Trade	131	A	x	x	x	x	
Deon's Designs	132	A	x	x	x	x	

Bead Types: A- All kinds O- Old E- Ethnic N- New U - Unique	Page No.	Beads	Tools	Find-ings	Cus-tom Work	Bks	Con-sign-ment
Oregon cont.							
Fire Mountain Gems	132	A	x	x		x	
Harlequin Beads	132	A		x	x	x	x
Looking Glass Beads	133	A	x	x	x	x	
Multnomah Bead	133	A	x	x		x	
Out Of The Blue	133	A	x	x		x	
Portland Bead Company	134	A	x	x	x	x	
Rainbow Bead Co	134	Japanese seed beads					
Southwest Trading Post	135	A	x	x			
Tierracast	135	Unique findings					
WorldBeads	135	A	x	x		x	
PENNSYLVANIA							
Cochrans Crafts	136	A					
Barbara Ann Volk	136	Designer					
SOUTH CAROLINA							
One By One	136	A	x	x	x	x	
Red Piano Too Gallery	137	E-U					
SOUTH DAKOTA							
Sioux Trading Post	137	Native American					
TENNESSEE							
Land of Odds	138	A	x	x	x	x	
TEXAS							
Alexander-Lee	138	Venetian glass beads					
Bally Bead Company	138	A	x	x			
Bead It!	139	A	x	x	x	x	
Celebration!	139	A	x	x	x	x	
Las Canadas - Bead Shop	139	A	x	x		x	
Mila's Boutique	140	A	x	x		x	
WorldBeads	140	A	x	x	x	x	
UTAH							
Eagle Feather	140	Native American					
Moabilia	141	A	x	x	x	x	
VERMONT							
Optional Extras	141	A	x	x	x	x	x
VIRGINIA							
Bead Garden & Herbary	141	A	x	x	x		
Star's Beads	143	A	Classes				
The Bead Shop	142	A	x	x	x	x	
Beads & Rocks	142	A	x	x			
Beadazzled	142	A	x	x	x	x	x
Touch The Earth	143	A	x	x		x	

Bead Types: A- All kinds O- Old E- Ethnic N- New U - Unique	Page No.	Beads	Tools	Findings	Custom Work	Bks	Consignment
WASHINGTON							
Bead Bazaar	144	A	x	x	x	x	
Bead Boppers	144	A	x	x		x	
Bead Factory	144	A	x	x	x	x	
The Bead Store	145	A	x	x		x	
Beaded Toucan	145	A	x	x			
Beads & Beyond	145	A	x	x	x	x	
Beads Indeed!	146	A	x	x	x	x	
Britz Beads	146						
The Garuda & I	146	A	x	x	x	x	
Hands Of The Hills	147	E			x	x	
Island Beads and More	148	A-E-U	x	x		x	
Margie's Design	148	A	x	x	x		
Monsoon	148	A	x				
Northwest Passage	149	A		x			
Outrageous Temptations	149	Costumes for belly dance					
Pacific Crossroads	149	A	x	x			
Rings & Things	150	A	x	x	x	x	
Shipwreck Beads	150	A	x	x		x	
WISCONSIN							
The Blue Bead	151	A	x	x	x	x	
Knot Just Beads	151	A	x	x	x	x	
Lulu's Beads	151	A	x	x	x	x	
Planet Bead	152	A	x	x	x		
Tropic Jewel	152	A	x	x	x		
Turtle Island Beads	152	A	x	x	x		
MAIL ORDER ONLY							
The Bead Room	166	A		x			
Christina's Designs	166	Swarosvki crystals					
Columbine Beads	166	A					
Empyrean Beads	167	A					
Grey Owl	167	Native American craft supplies					
Hecho A Mano	167	Guatemalan handicrafts					
Kalipay	168	Beads from the Philippines					
Material Culture	168	Cat's eye beads					
Matoska	168	Native American					
Pennylane Beads	169	A					
Renee Foxx Beads	169	A					
Rishashay	170	Handmade sterling beads & clasps					

245 Cross Reference

Bead Types: A- All kinds O- Old E- Ethnic N- New U - Unique	Page No.	Beads	Tools	Find- ings	Cus- tom Work	Con- sign- Bks	ment
Mail Order Cont.							
San Francisco Crafts	170	A					
Shreds and Patches	170	Porcupine and quills only					
Soft Flex Wire	171	Wire					
Universal Synergetics	171	A	x	x	x	x	
Wakeda Trading Post	171	Native American beads and crafts					
BEADMAKERS							
Tom Andre	172	Glass beadmaker					
Arrow Springs	172	Glass beadmaker and teacher					
Holland & Sage	173	Glass beadmaker					
Beadzerk!	173	Glass beadmaker					
Joel Bloomberg	173	Glass beadmaker					
Bohemian On The Range	174	Beadmaker and silversmith					
Tom Boylan	174	Glass beadmaker					
Boutz Family	174	Glass beadmaker and teacher					
CD Beads	175	Glass and polymer beadmakers					
Judith Content	190	Paper beadmaker					
Crystal Myths	175	Glass beadmaker					
Dancing Rabbit	176	Glass beadmaker					
Fancy's	176	Glass beadmaker					
Fetish Designs	177	Glass beadmaker					
Fineline Studios	177	Glass beadmaker					
Kate Fowle	178	Glass beadmaker and teacher					
Gaea Glassworks	178	Glass beadmaker and teacher					
Gardens of Glass	179	Glass beadmaker and teacher					
Nancy Goodenough	180	Glass beadmaker					
Gossamer Glass	181	Glass beadmaker and teacher					
Harmon/Nyala	181	Glass beadmaker					
Tyler Hannigan	192	Polymer beadmaker					
Inner Light	182	Glass beadmaker					
Johnston Glass	182	Glass beadmaker					
Ginger Kelly	182	Glass beadmaker					
Laughing Glass	183	Glass beadmaker					
Kristina Logan	183	Glass beadmaker					
Kris Peterson/Luna Bead	184	Glass beadmaker					
Mirabai Arts	191	Polymer beadmaker					
Modern Alchemy	184	Glass beadmaker and teacher					
More Beads	191	Polymer and glass beadmaker					
Nesting Heart	191	Polymer beadmaker					
Newcomb Company	192	Porcelain beadmaker					

Bead Types: A- All kinds O- Old E- Ethnic N- New U - Unique	Page No.	Beads	Tools	Findings	Custom Work	Bks	Consignment
Beadmakers cont.							
Odyssey Designs	185	Glass beadmaker					
Olive Glass	185	Glass beadmaker					
Potek Glass	185	Glass beadmaker					
Paula Radke	186	Glass beadmaker					
Rene Roberts	187	Glass beadmaker					
Don Schneider	187	Glass beadmaker					
Splendid Loon	193	Porcelain beadmaker					
Bruce St. John Maher	187	Glass beadmaker					
Irene Stant	188	Glass beadmaker					
Heather Trimlett	188	Glass beadmaker					
Twilight Fire	188	Glass beadmaker					
Victoria Alexis	189	Glass beadmaker					
Pati Walton	189	Glass beadmaker					
Joyce Whitaker	193	Porcelain beadmaker					
Winged Woman	189	Glass beadmaker					
Wood Forms	193	Wood beadmaker					
GLASS BEADMAKING SUPPLIERS							
Arrow Springs	194						
Beads Supplies Int'l	194						
Frantz Bead Supply	194						
The Glass Menagerie	196						
Merchants of Venice	197						
Northwest Art Glass	198						
Lewis C. Smith	198						
Wale Apparatus	198						
CANADA							
Beadworks	202	A			x	x	x	x
Mano A Mano	203	A			x	x	x	
Sassy Bead Co.	204	A			x	x	x	x
Silver Moon Trading	204	A-E-U	x		x	x	x	
ENGLAND							
Beads!	205	A			x	x	Bks	
Spangles	205	A						
TAIWAN							
Material Culture	206	E-U						

Coupons

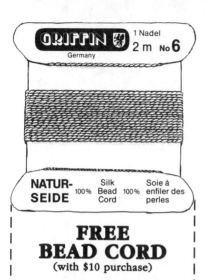

Coupons

Coupons

Coupons

Coupons

REPLY CARD

Return this card now and we will send you:
A free surprise gift. Send us the name(s) of your bead friends and we will send each of you a free gift.
Please, please print clearly!!
Return to: The Bead Directory P.O. Box 10103, Oakland, CA 94610

Name: _____

Address: _____

Address: _____

City: _____

State-Zip: _____

Where did you purchase The Bead Directory?

Your favorite Bead Store (include name and address):

Your favorite Bead Book:

How many bead books do you purchase in one year?

On what subject would you like to see new bead books published?

Would you attend a bead bazaar in your area?

What would you like to see in future editions?

What kind of beads do you purchase most?

Are you a beadmaker? What kind of beads do you make?

Comments and suggestions:

Reply Card

ORDER FORM

It's easy to order your own copy. Complete the form below and either cut it out or copy the form and mail it now. Your Bead Directory will be shipped upon receipt of payment.

The Bead Directory, P.O. Box 10103, Oakland, CA 94610

Yes send me _____ copies of The Bead Directory **$18.95 each plus shipping and handling** listed below.
           Shipping/Handling:
      US Book Rate add $2.50 (allow 2-4 weeks)
      US First Class add $3.75 (arrives in 4-5 days)
      Canada Airmail add $4.50 (allow 2-4 weeks)
      Outside US/Canada: Airmail add $9.50
      All foreign orders must be in US Dollars Only!

Total Enclosed (Including S/H): $_____
Payable to: The Bead Directory

Name: _____

Address: _____

Address: _____

City: _____

State, Zip: _____

Telephone: _____

❑ Please send information on how I can include my business in the next Bead Directory. (Include your phone number)

❑ I have a retail store and want to sell The Bead Directory to my customers. Please send wholesale rates. (Must include your phone number).

Order Form